THE OTHER SIDE OF READING

"If the words remain words and sit quietly on the page; if they remain nouns, and verbs and adjectives, then we are truly blind. But if the words seem to disappear and our innermost self begins to laugh and cry, to sing and dance, and finally to fly --- if we are transported in all that we are, to a brand new world, then --- only then --- can we say that we can READ!"

Joe Wayman.

Copyright © Good Apple, Inc. 1980
ISBN No. 0-916456-64-1
Printing No. 15 14

GOOD APPLE, INC.
BOX 299
CARTHAGE, IL 62321

All Rights Reserved — Printed in United States of America by Hamilton Press, Inc., Hamilton, Illinois.

CONTENTS

•Introduction

When you read a good book does the rest of your world just seem to disappear? Do your thoughts take flight? Are you transported to another land where you can see the characters, smell the smells, and feel the textures of wonderful and exciting places? Do books come alive for you in your mind's eye? I hope so. That is what this book is all about. If you can VISUALIZE what you are reading, if the material simply comes alive for you, then you are a true reader. You are using the skill called IMAGERY.

Children in our culture are losing this very precious skill. When you read to students, hopefully every day, what is the first thing they want you to do? "Show us the pictures." And the sadness in that is that if there are no pictures, you lose half of a classroom before you even get started. Our children are turning off the process of visualization. What we call "imagination." And yet many of them have the cognitive, rational skills. They can do phonics worksheets, unlock isolated words, spell, and do all the other logical skills they need to be able to read. But they leave the classroom and then never pick up a book! Why? Because for many of them the imagination is dying or has already died or been turned off. They either don't, won't or can't use their imagination to give magic to the words on a page.

We have forgotten about all the skills we must use to be excited about reading. The research on the brain now gives us a metaphor for talking about those skills. It is the "split-brain" concept. Or left brain-right brain research. It suggests that the left side of the mind is rational, logical, sequential, linear and abstract. It is this side of the mind that unlocks and decodes words. Our language (these little symbols) come out of that side of the mind. When children work skill sheets, do phonics, learn word-attack skills and otherwise decode words, they are using the left side of the brain. These skills are very important and we teach them and teach them and teach them and teach them . . . . . .

And we forget that there is an equally important kind of thinking that must be going on if those children will ever be readers. And those skills come out of the right side of the brain. The right side seems to be intuitive, spatial, visual and concrete. It is from this side of the mind that we are able to VISUALIZE. And visualization at a very sophisticated level is required if reading is going to be that magical carpet that transports us with great joy into new worlds. Worlds created by words. And this "right-brain" thinking is THE OTHER SIDE OF READING: The Forgotten Skills.

Try this: read the following carefully.

The midway was deserted. The dust from the day before had settled and the silence hung like a heavy woolen quilt over the empty carnival. The gray light of dawn trembled at the edge of the now still ferris-wheel and began to reach out long delicate fingers toward the canopy of the sleeping carousel. The colors of the horses were beginning to brighten. From the dark shadows of the night emerged, moment by moment, all the colors of a living carousel. As if it were about to come back to life, it slowly began the change from gray to blue, green and red. The animals hung as if in suspended animation. Waiting. Waiting. Slowly the carousel begins to turn. Setting the animals free. Beginning their crazy race around and around and around. Listen to the music begin. The lights are blinking on. The carousel is beginning to turn, alone, by itself . . . it can wait no longer . . . . . .

Now, what happened in your mind?

Give yourself a few

moments to

think

about it.

Could you see a carousel? Could you see yourself standing in an empty carnival midway? What about the colors of the carousel? Could you hear the music? Could you see the scene get brighter and brighter? If so, you are using the skill called VISUAL IMAGERY. The KEY to being a successful and excited reader: IMAGERY.

The frightening thing about the research today is that it tells us that children are turning away from that skill. They are no longer learning how to do it. Television, movies, highly specific toys and an increase in pressure to develop cognitive (left-brain) skills at an earlier and earlier age are working in sinister harmony to more and more effectively short-circuit the ability children have to imagine — to visualize!

This book is a collection of activities that, I believe, should be incorporated into every child's day to help develop the ability to:

1.	SEE	Seeing in turn develops the ability to visualize. The more effectively we see and recall what we see, the more effectively we can visualize.
2.	VISUALIZE	Closing your eyes and creating a visual image in your mind. When we visualize clearly, we can not only see the image; but we can hear it, touch it, taste it, and smell it.

VISUALIZATION is the mysterious and illusive key factor in turning non-readers into readers. It must be practiced every day. Built into the reading program and curriculum every day K-12 and beyond.

SKILLS YOU WILL BE WORKING WITH IN THIS BOOK

SEEING SKILLS

Pattern Completion:	The completion of a visual, auditory or kinesthetic pattern.
Sequencing visually:	Identifying and extending visual, sequential patterns.
Analytical seeing:	Identifying the basic elements or parts of what is being seen.
Synthesizing visually:	Being able to take parts of what is seen and put them together to form "wholes."
Visual recall:	Learning to see clearly, in detail, and to retain the image.

VISUALIZATION SKILLS

Visualization:	Seeing with the mind's eye. Development of detail and clarity in what is being visualized.
Multi-sensory imagery:	Developing images from sounds, colors, taste and touch. Using all the senses to enhance imagination development.

SOME HINTS FOR USING THIS BOOK

Use at least one activity from this book every day.

Don't be in a hurry to give students the answers. If you give them an activity on Monday, put the answer on the board or work through it with the class no sooner than the next Monday. Give them time to deal with it.

Read the instructions at the first of each chapter before you jump into that chapter.

Don't EVER grade any of these exercises!!

If you can stand the temptation, don't look at the answers at all! Work the problems along with your students. You too can develop your visualization skills.

Maintain a "fun," yet important attitude toward these experiences.

In some cases duplicate the problem on an overhead and use it with the entire class. Other times let them work on the activities in pairs or small groups. And still at other times, let students work through them individually.

Encourage students to take these home and get parents involved.

Note that in some cases specific directions and/or questions for a particular page will follow that page. If an activity is not clear, look for further instructions on the following page.

Each of the chapters in this book teaches to one or more of the above skills. In most cases many of the skills are being developed simultaneously. In the beginning of each chapter you will find the various skills listed for that chapter. The first skill will be the strongest for that chapter and the skills listed below it will be necessary but subordinate to the first one. Directions for use of each chapter are at the first of each chapter and answers to specific problems are listed at the end of the book.

Any or all of these pages can be duplicated for your use in the classroom.

PLEASE

Use this book as a jumping off place into imagination and visualization. It is only a beginning. . . a starting place. These are the kinds of things that can begin to bring VISUALIZATION back to children as an active and vital part of their thinking. It is critical for all children and adults alike. Try them out with your gifted students. Try them out with children who are carrying labels of disability . . . you may be surprised at the results. Also, remember that this kind of thinking should be done by ALL kids! (and adults)

Then go to the bibliography. It is full of materials that will take you further into "right-brain" thinking. Be sure your students are doing some of this kind of visualization and problem solving every day.

And one last thing. We are finally beginning to realize the importance of "imagination" in the reading and language process. Experiences in art, music, dance and creative drama all teach to this skill and all the skills defined in this book. Use them every day; incorporate them into each learning experience. The materials in the following pages can be incorporated a little at a time into your classroom to teach those vital visualization skills.

Sincerely
Joe Wayman

A-MAZ-ING

Skills: Analytical seeing, visual recall.

The following activities are sequential . . . they become increasingly difficult. Students should approach each one in the following manner:

(SPECIAL DIRECTIONS FOR USING MAZES IN YOUR CLASSROOM)

Step 1.   Students place the maze in front of them and try to solve it with their eyes alone. (Sometimes I have them sit on their hands to keep from using a pencil.)

Step 2.   After they have tried it with eyes alone, they may use their fingers.

Step 3.   If they still have trouble and cannot solve it either of the first two ways, cover the mazes with clear plastic adhesive so they can use washable markers to solve the maze. They can then wash it off and others in the class can work it also.

These ten mazes are just a beginning . . . for a vast source of mazes see the series of booklets published by Troubador Press, 485 Fremont St., San Francisco, CA, entitled, MAZE CRAZE!

Sipping cider through a straw? From which glass? Find out with just your eyes.

Which fish is our friend catching? The others are catching each other. Which ones are connected to which? Use only your eyes!

Use your eyes. Help Ms. Mouse get home again.

If you turn on the faucet, which buckets will you fill? Use just your eyes.

From star to star. Can you do it?

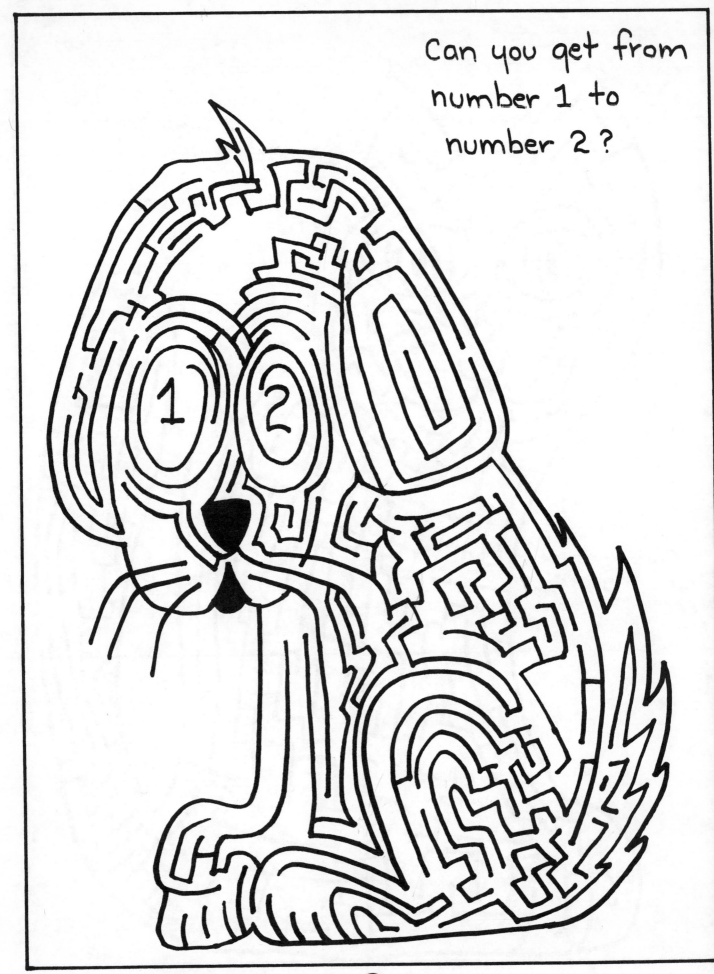

Can you get from number 1 to number 2 ?

Help the ladybug find its friend. There is only one way.

● HOW MANY ?

Skills: Analytical seeing, pattern identification.

The pages in this section are sequential beginning with the easiest and growing more complex.

After each page, let students create new ones of their own and put them up on a bulletin board titled, HOW MANY? Structure some time for solving each other's problems . . . OR . . .

Let each child make one based on the one they have done from the book, and then exchange them. Pass them around and then work on each other's . . . OR . . .

Let each student make one and then put them into a book . . . OR . . .

You may wish to duplicate enough of these pages for every student. Duplicate both the problem . . . and the questions on the back of the problem page. After a student has tried each question, encourage her/him to create some new questions for that page.

How many rectangles in this picture?

How many rectangles can you see?

How many enclosed shapes can you find?

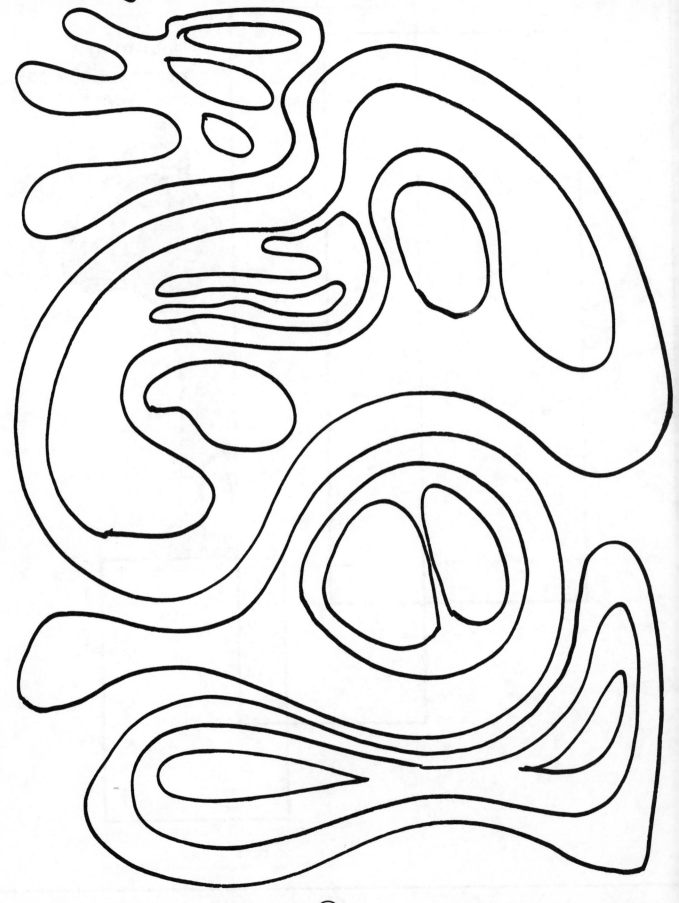

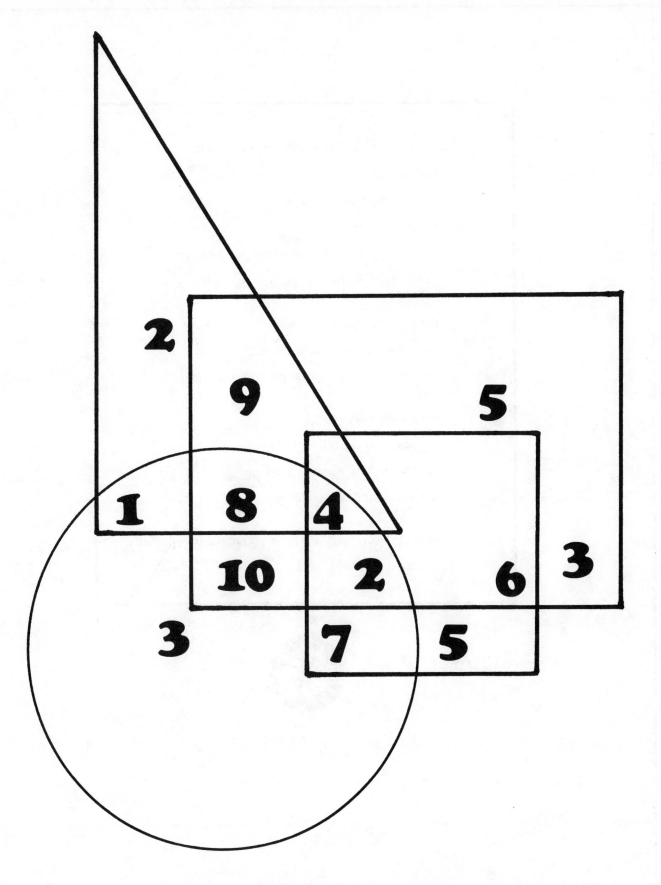

2

9

5

1 8 4

3

10 2 6 3

3 7 5

(See next page for questions)

What is the total of the numbers that are in . . . .

the rectangle only?

the rectangle and the square only?

the triangle only?

the triangle, the square and the rectangle only?

the triangle, square, rectangle and circle?

the circle only?

the circle, rectangle and the triangle only?

the circle, rectangle, triangle, and the square?

the square only?

the square and circle only?

the square, circle and triangle only?

the square and rectangle only?

How many more questions can you make up yourself?

How many enclosed
shapes can you
find in this
picture?

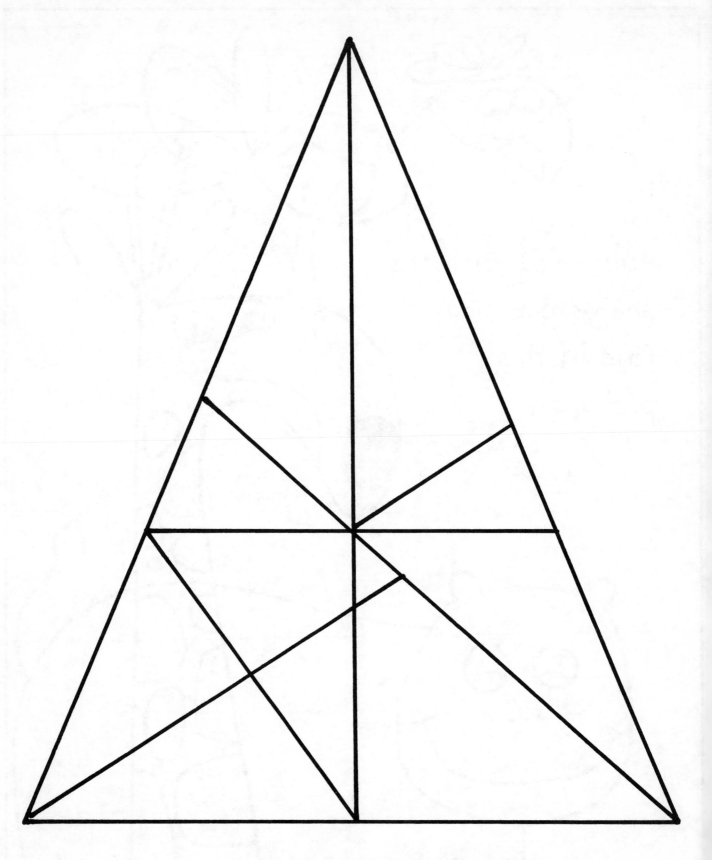

How many triangles can you find?

How many circles can you see?

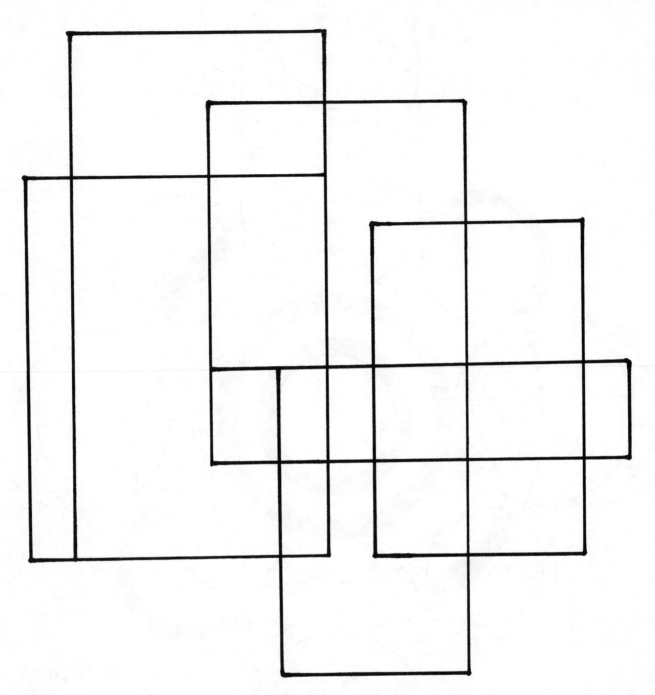

If you can count at least 35 rectangles, you have "supervision"!

How many enclosed shapes can you find?

●TANGRAMS

Skills: Synthesizing visually, visualization.

The Tangram is an ancient Chinese puzzle and has endless creative possibilities.

1.   Duplicate ρ 31 for each student. Have them mount it on a piece of tag board, cover front and back with clear plastic adhesive and then cut out the seven shapes that make up the tangram.

2.   The seven shapes can be put together forming a square, but this is the most difficult tangram. Don't expect anyone in your class to solve that one right away.

3.   Now duplicate the pages following. In each case the shaded area can be made exactly with some or all of the tangram pieces. The pieces CANNOT be overlapped. Where there are two shapes on a page, they cannot be made simultaneously as they may require the same tangram pieces.

After having worked through this section have students, working in pairs, come up with a new shape, draw around it in a heavy line and shade it in, add a background. These can then be passed around for a classroom full of brand new tangram puzzles on which to work.

Keep your tangram puzzle safely stored in a ziplock baggy and take 5 minutes in each day to "play" with them creating new shapes or solving the shapes your friends have created.

If anyone solves the square, they have super ability to visualize and manipulate ideas spatially . . . or they are very LUCKY!

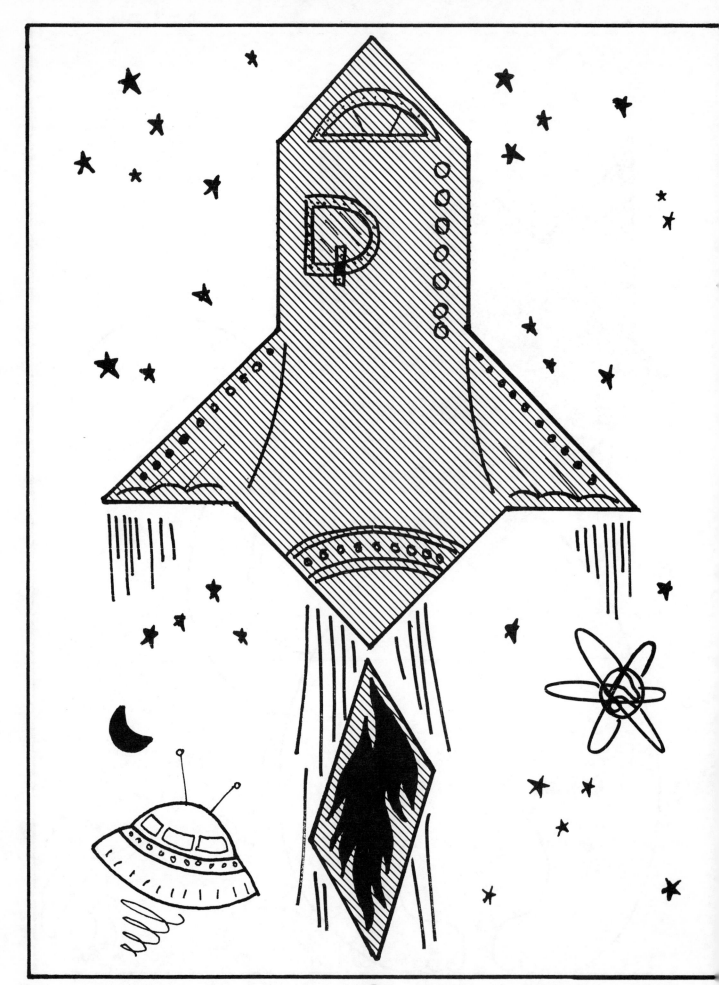

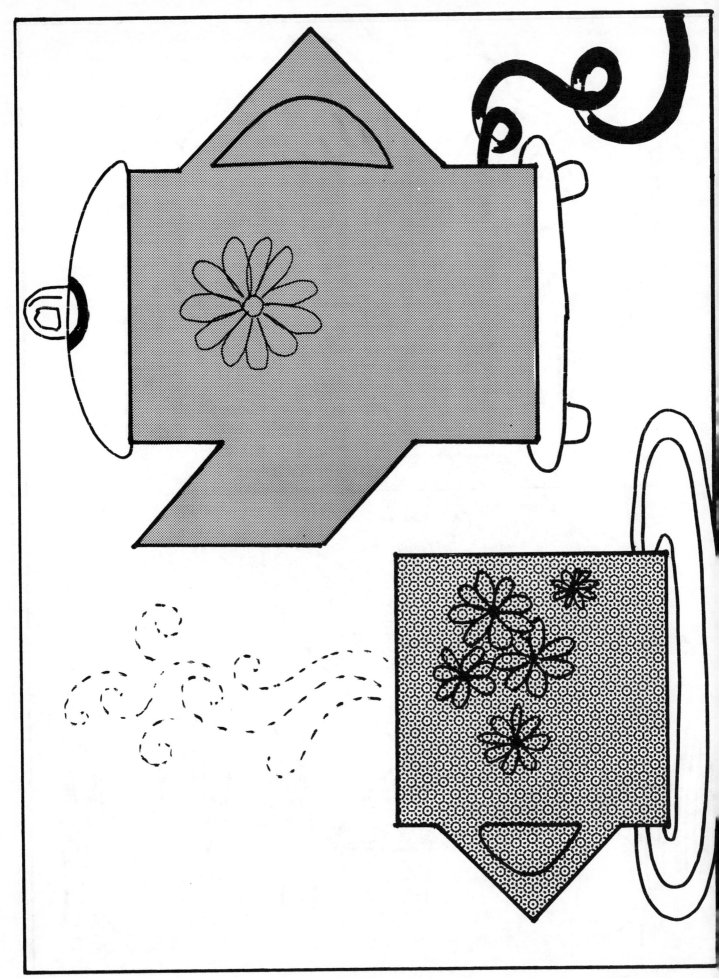

●SHAPE UP!

Skills: Visualization, synthesizing visually, pattern completion, analytical seeing.

The first part of this section is very similar to tangrams, but the shapes are different and designed to fit together into a predetermined shape.

Use this sequence for this section:

1.   Duplicate the pages for all students.

2.   Encourage them to look at the pieces and try to see how they would fit together and be reorganized to make the shape required.

3.   If they cannot do it with their eyes alone, then they may take a pencil and try sketching solutions.

4.   When all else fails, cut out the shapes and manipulate them until they fit exactly over the indicated space. (They may NOT be overlapped.)

The second part of this chapter deals with CONGRUENT shapes. In each case the task is to determine if the shaded area is identical to the light area.

Use the pages sequentially as they get progressively more difficult.

These should be done with the eyes rather than cutting them out to test them.

After you have worked with all of these pages, let the students figure out how congruent figures are made and let them create congruent and non-congruent figures themselves. These can be shared and students can work on solving each other's.

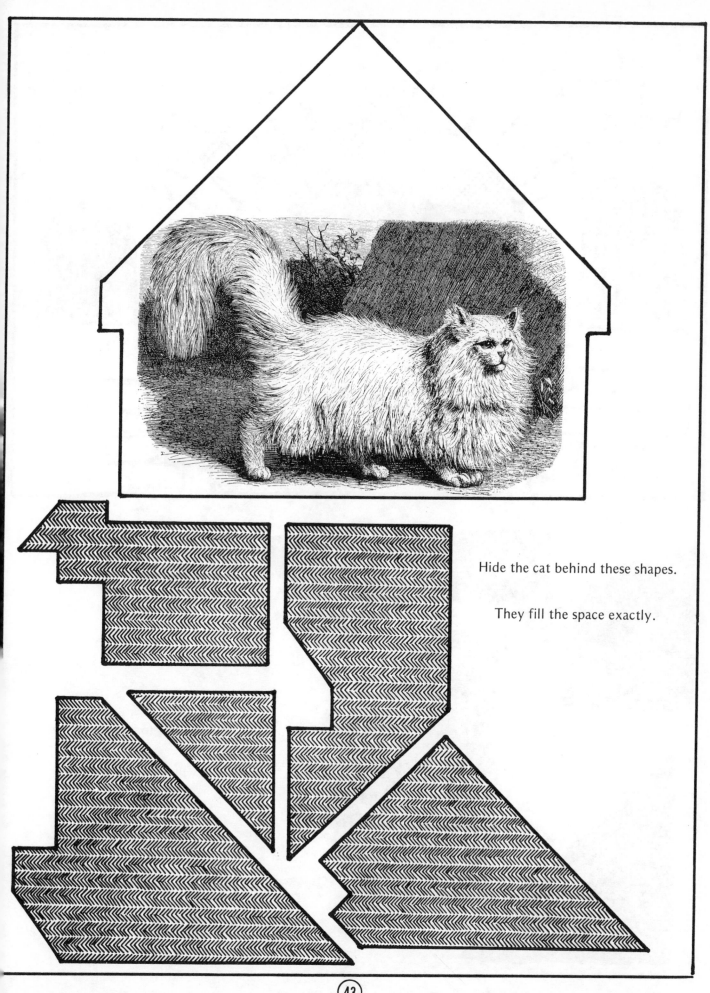

Hide the cat behind these shapes.

They fill the space exactly.

Use these shapes to build the door.

The pieces will fill the door exactly.

Cover the worm with a perfect pie crust. These five pieces will do it.

Swat the fly! Quickly before it flies away! The pieces will make the perfect swatter.

Can you cover the sea monster with the parts of this sail boat? They will cover the rectangle exactly.

I WAS FRAMED!!

Frame up this incorrigible inmate with these six shapes.

Make a frame around lovely Ms. Hog. These six pieces will do it.

Can you see how these three pieces fit together to make a square?

Can you see how to use these shapes to make a perfect circle?

These pieces will make a square. See if you can figure out how. If you have trouble, cut them out and try them in different ways.

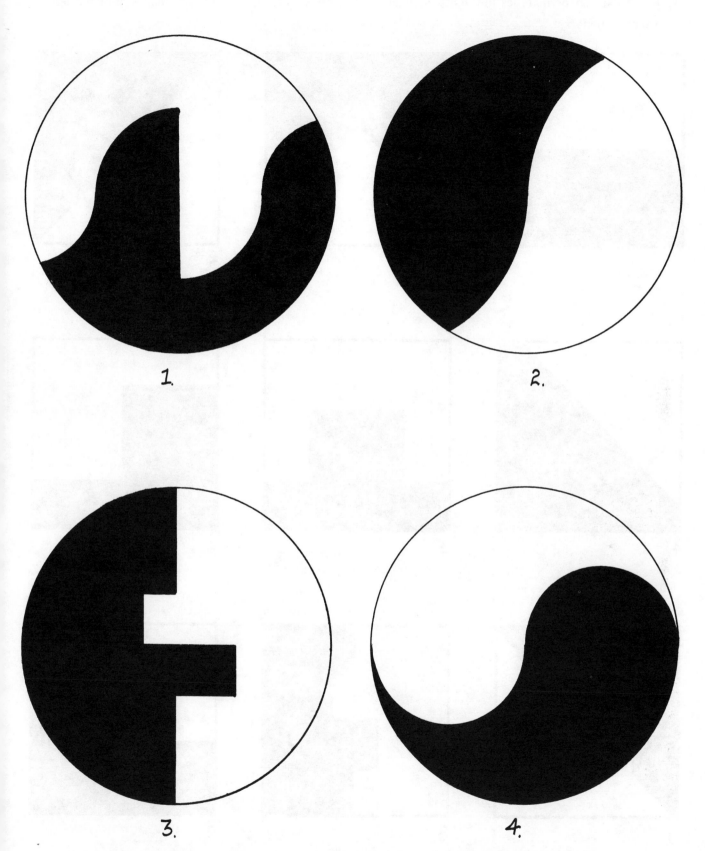

Are the dark shapes the same as the light ones? See if you can tell which ones match exactly in each circle.

If the dark shape matches the light one exactly, they are said to be "congruent" shapes. Which ones are congruent?

1.

2.

3.

4.

5.

6.

7.

8.

9.

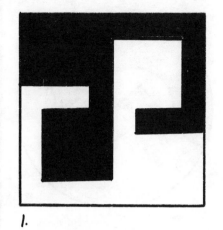

1.

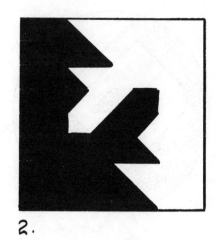

2.

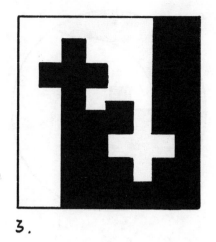

3.

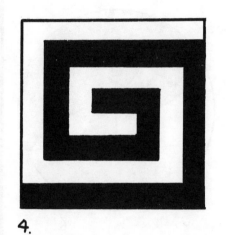

4.

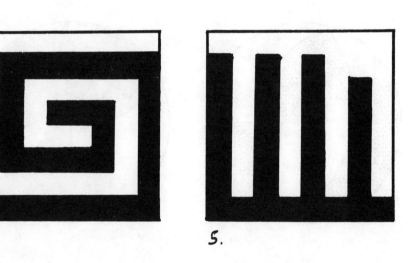

5.

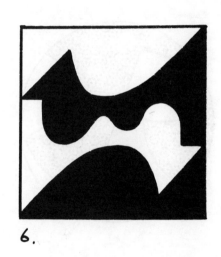

6.

7.

8.

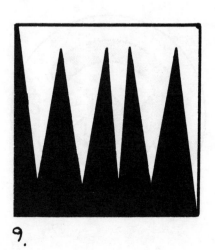

9.

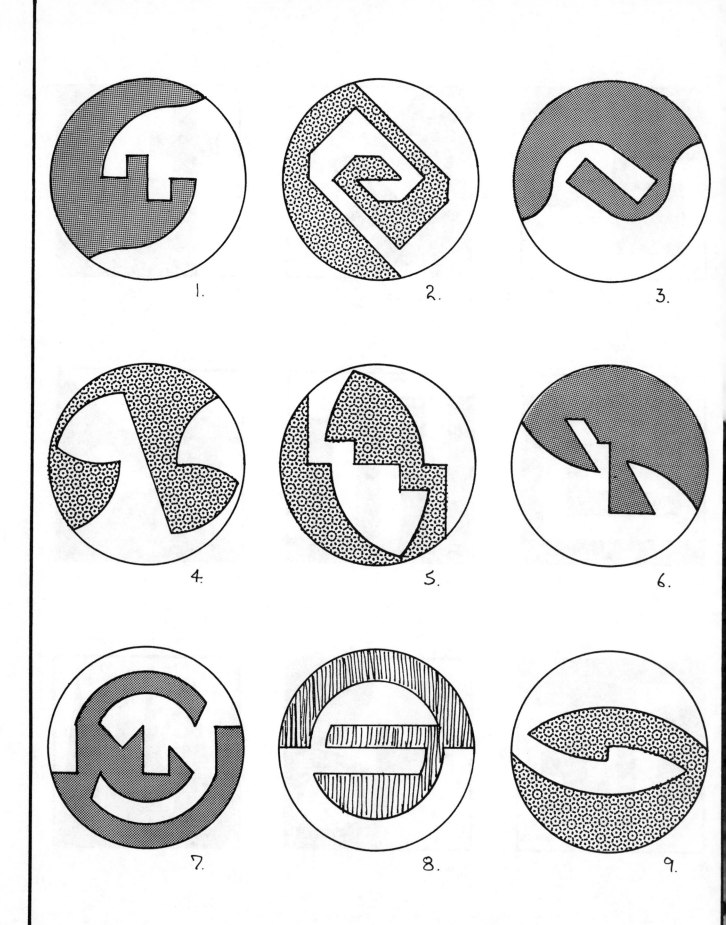

1.

2.

3.

4.

5.

6.

7.

8.

9.

1.

2.

3.

4.

5.

6.

7.

8.

9.

• WHICH ONE
IS
DIFFERENT
?

Skills: Pattern completion, analytical seeing.

The basic question for each of the pages in this section is to determine which one(s) are different. In ALL cases there can be more than one answer. In some of them there are an infinite number of answers. You will be interested in two kinds of differences:

1. Those that you can SEE in the picture (right hemisphere thinking).

2. Those differences that cannot be seen in the picture, but that rely on other information the student may have about the pictures (left hemisphere thinking).

Find all the differences you can — then try similarities.

Which one is different?

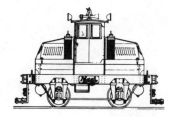

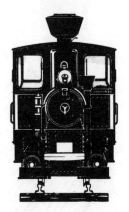

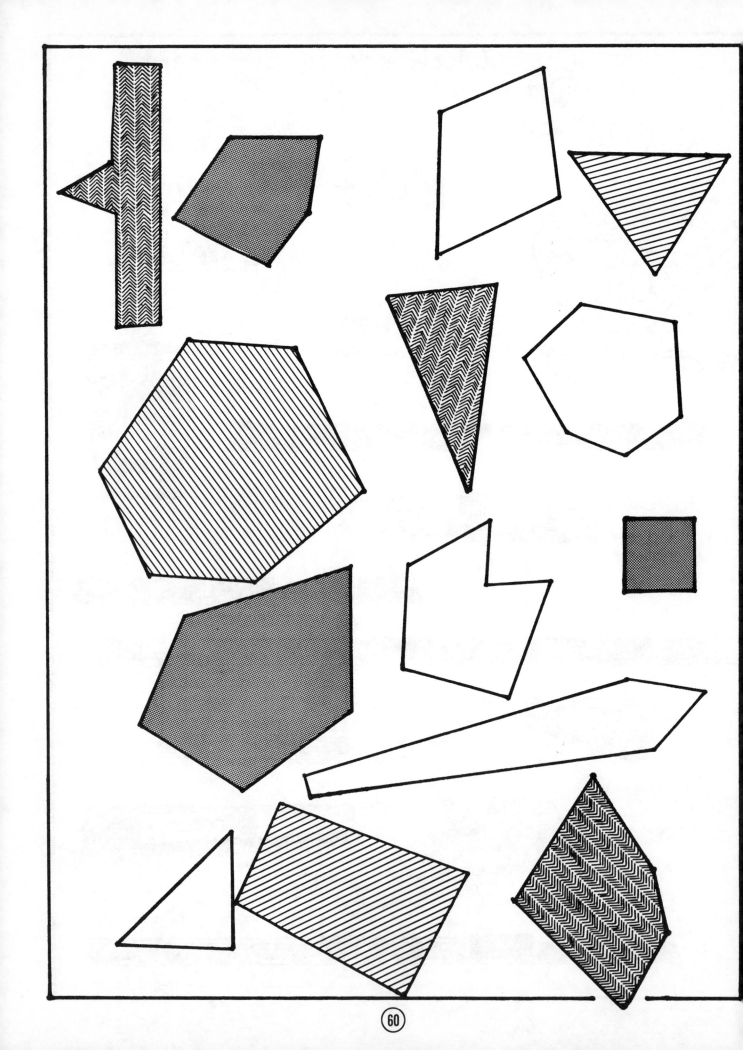

Which one is different?

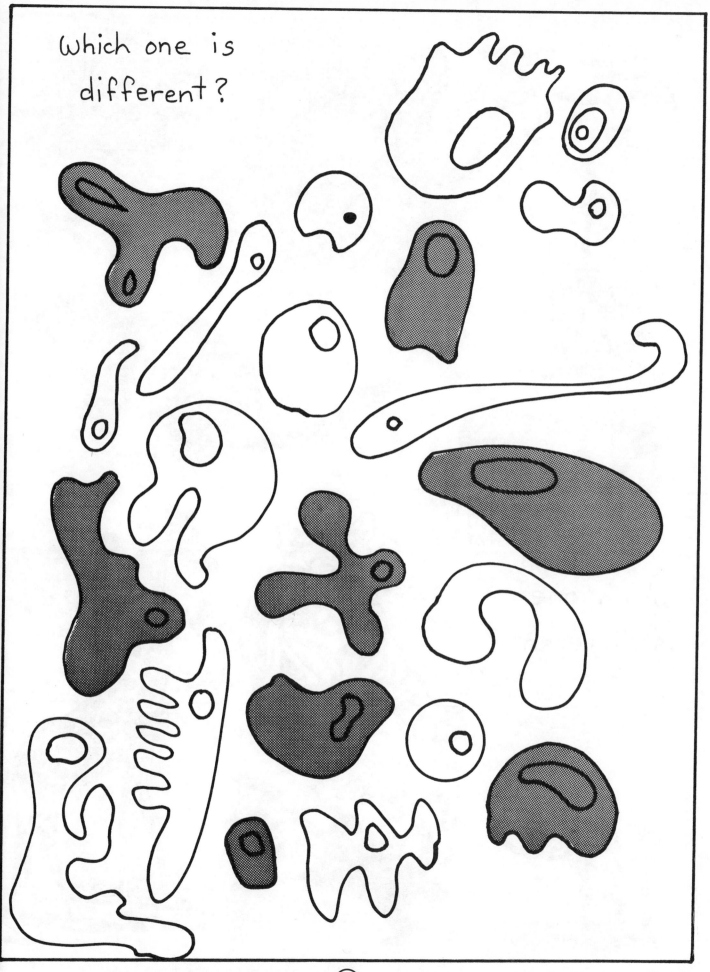

Which one
is different?

Which one is different?

Which one is different?

N F K M D P C W I E V l S T K J N P J W Y m U d c A U E F s

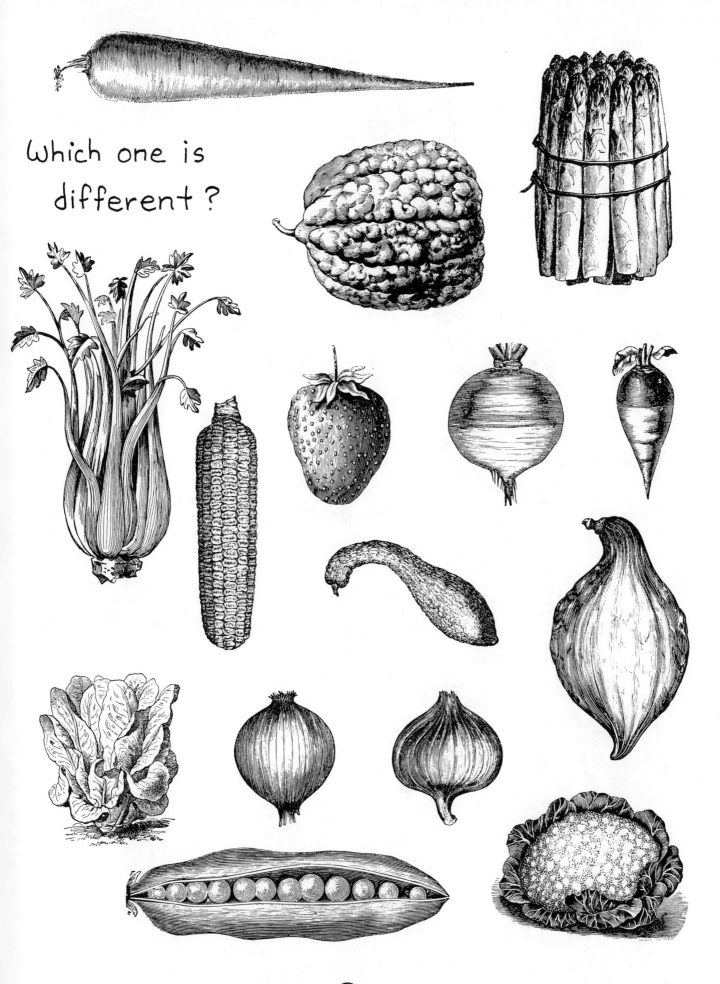

Which one is different ?

Which one does not belong? Can there be more than one answer?

MENTAL BLOCKS

Skills: Visualization, visual recall, pattern completion.

For this section you will need at least one box of 100 one-inch counting blocks. Ask your 1st grade teacher to lend them to you. They come in assorted colors. You will also need two or three packages of multi-colored silent counting discs.

If the students work alone on this one, they will each need about 10 blocks.

They will experience more success if they are in partners, however.

This chapter has several parts; each part is lettered and the instructions for each section follows:

The "A" Pages

Make overhead transparencies of each of these pages.

Each team of two has blocks in front of them. Isolate ONE of the configurations on the overhead, blocking out the others with 3 x 5 cards.

Flash the projector on and off as fast as you can.

Students are to duplicate the configuration they see.

Color is NOT part of this section.

If they need a second and third look, let them have them. Each time allowing only a fraction of a second.

Finally, turn the projector on long enough for them to check to see that they have arranged the cubes correctly.

When all the "A" pages have been done, let students draw new configurations on transparencies and use these to continue this kind of problem solving.

The "B" Pages

Duplicate the pages on overheads.

On each page in this section are three or four views of the same structure built from one-inch cubes. It is ONE structure.

Put the overhead on the projector and turn it on. Allow students to look at the three views and to build the structure. Remember, the three views are views of the same structure from three different perspectives.

These pages get progressively more difficult.

Leave the projector on while the students work these pages, so they can check their efforts as they work.

The "C" Pages

Make a transparency of each page and flash it as quickly as possible on the screen. Students must then duplicate the structure.

Give them a second look, and then finally a third if they need it.

Turn projector on after they have finished so they can check their structure against the drawing.

The "D" Pages

First duplicate a page for each student.

The first task is to complete each drawing. They are all structures built from one-inch cubes.

When the drawing is complete, have the students build the structure.

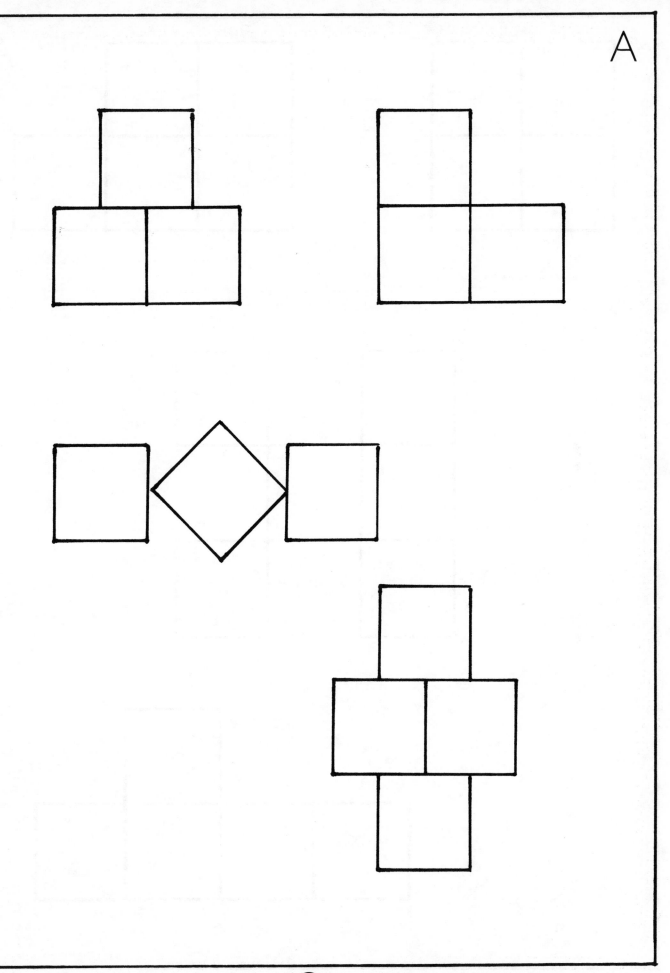

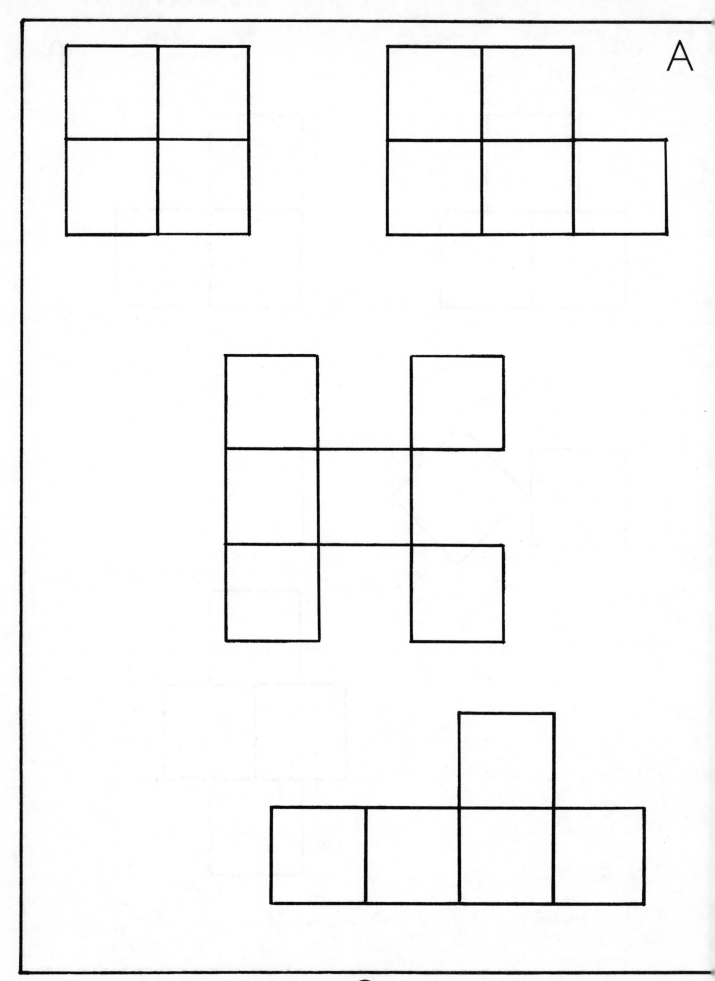

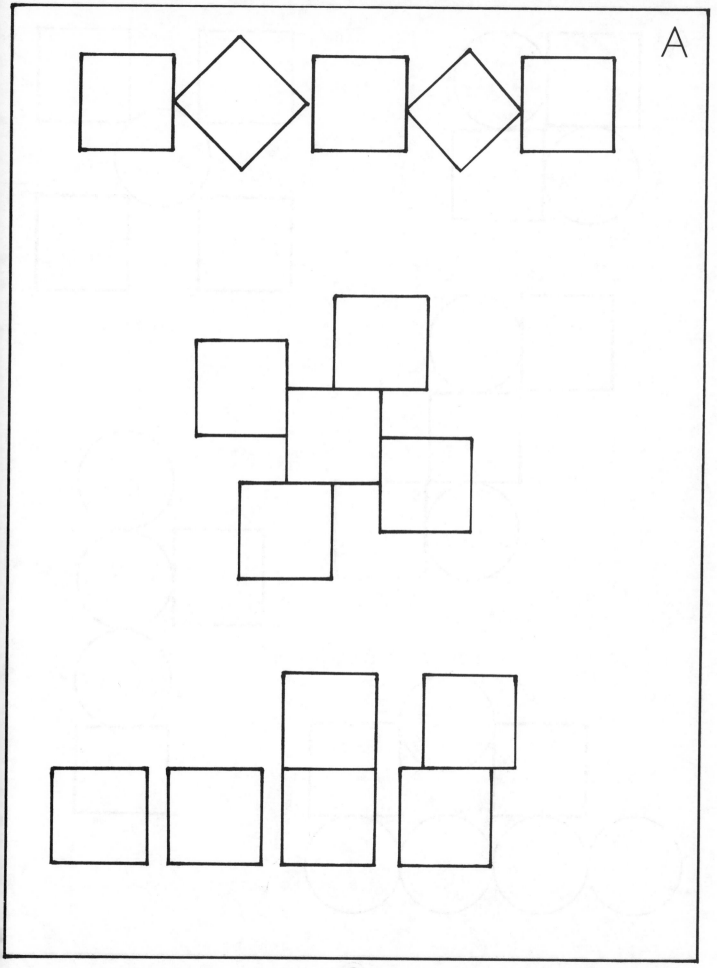

A

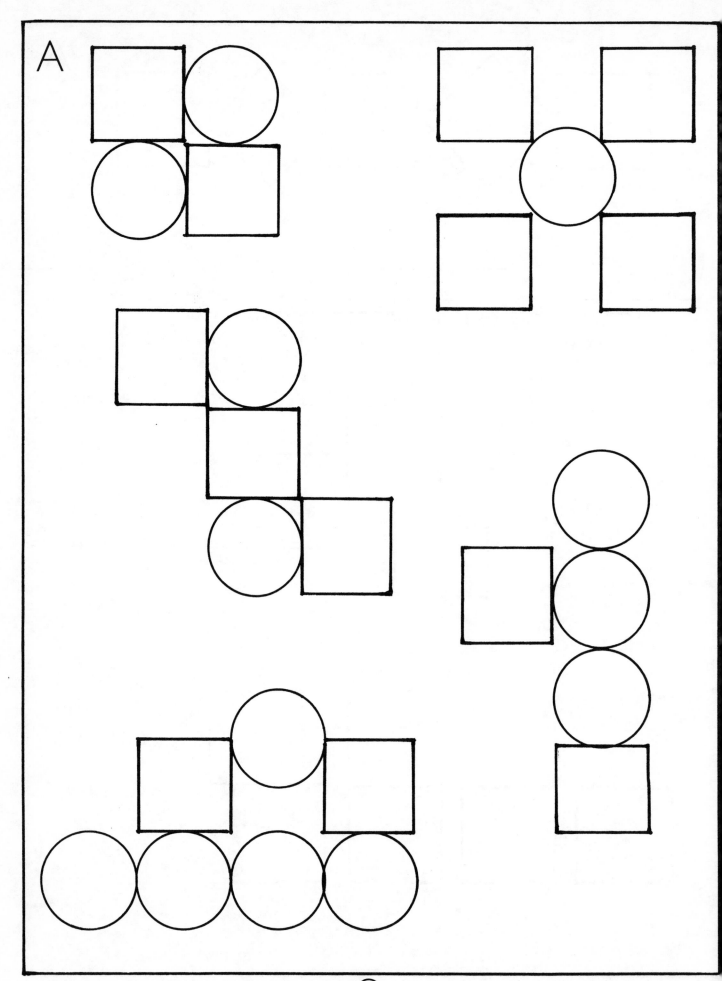

B

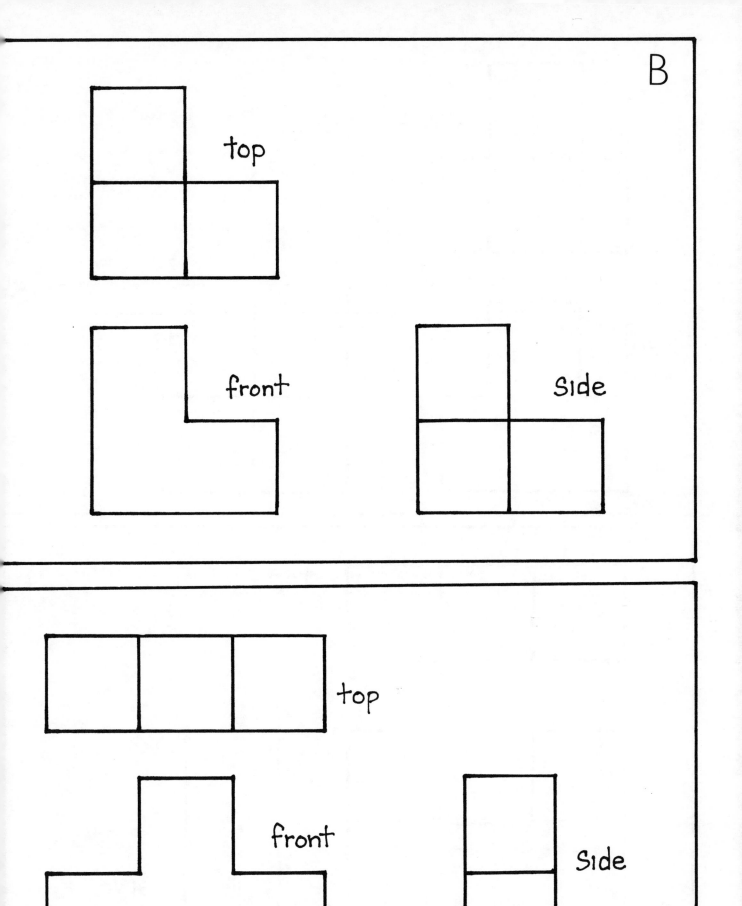

top

front

side

top

front

side

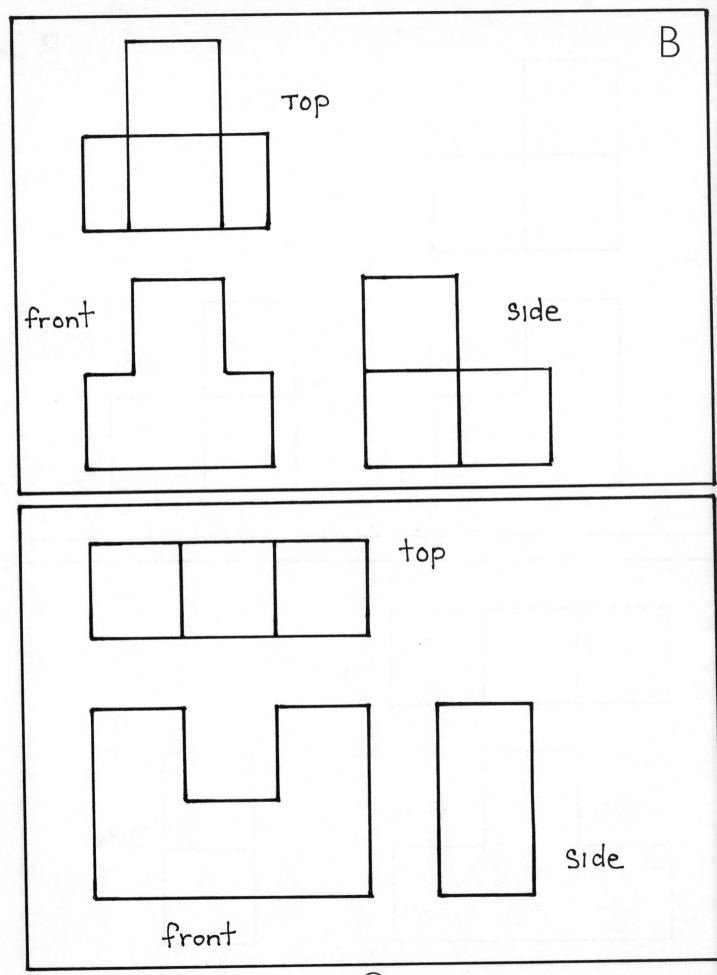

B

TOP

front

side

top

front

side

B

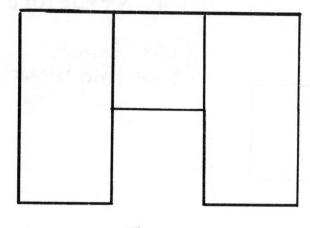

Top

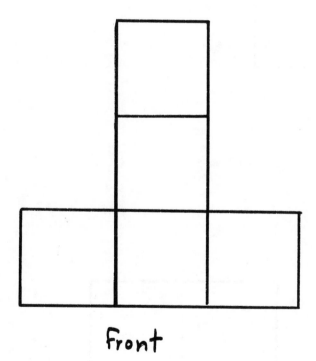

Front   Side

Can you build B
this structure?

(use 1-inch
counting blocks)

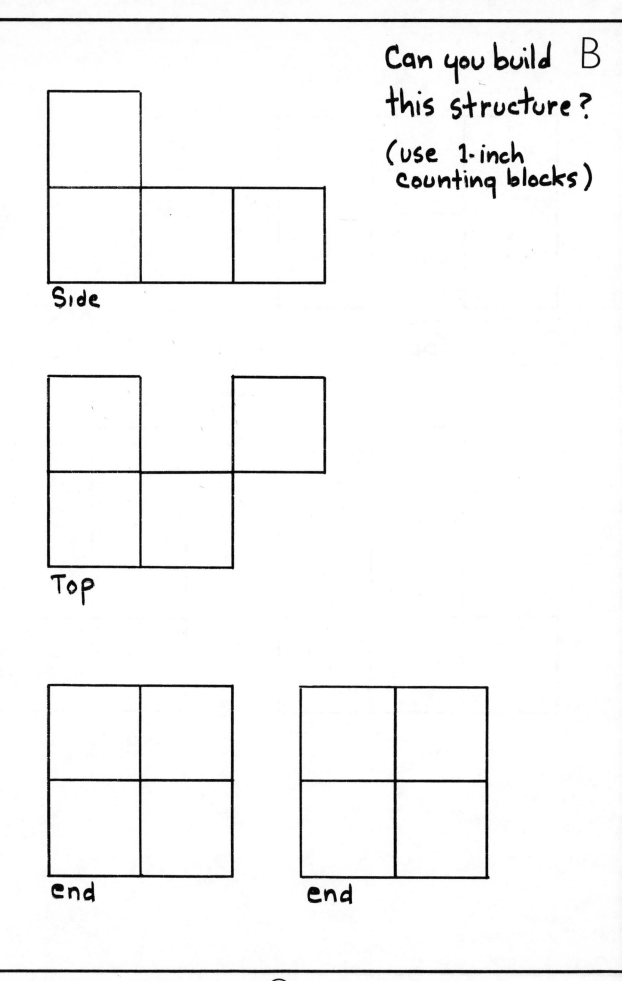

Side

Top

end   end

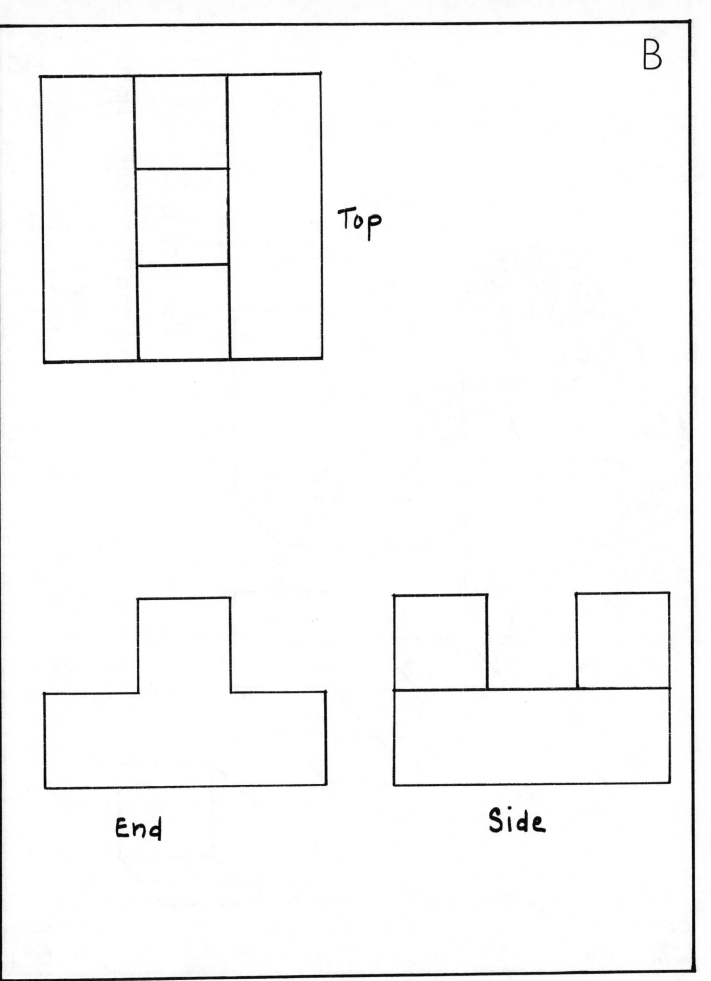

B

Top

End

Side

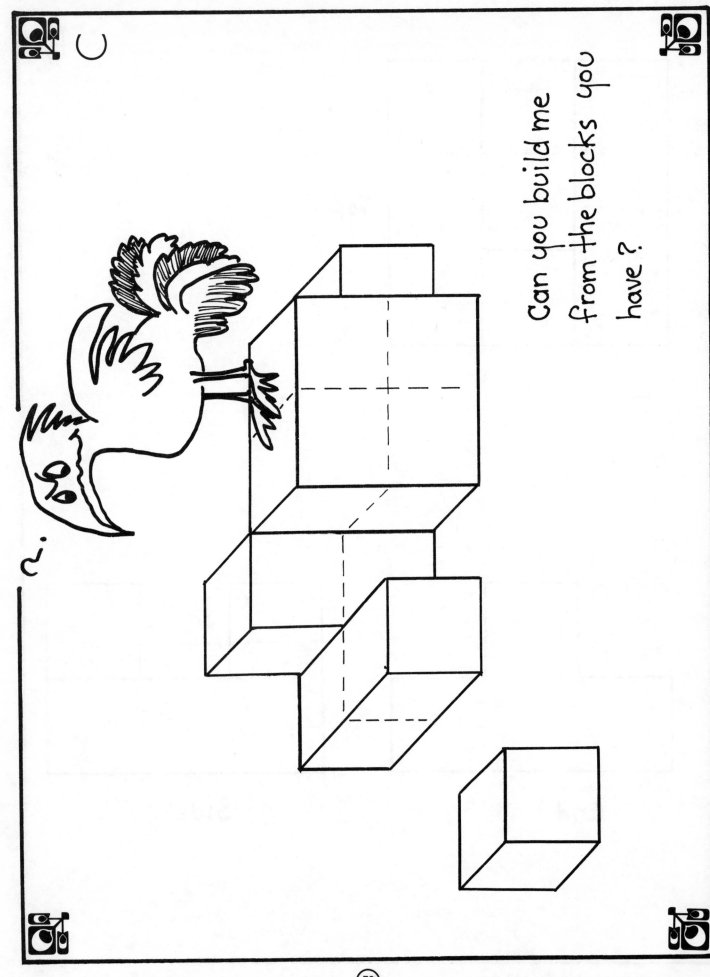

Can you build me from the blocks you have?

C

Build me ?

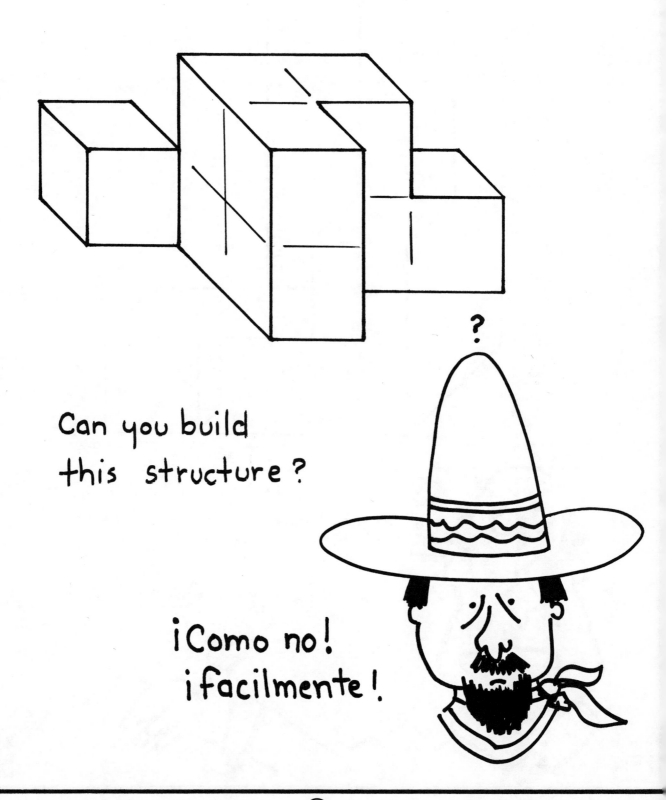

Can you build
this structure?

¡Como no!
¡facilmente!

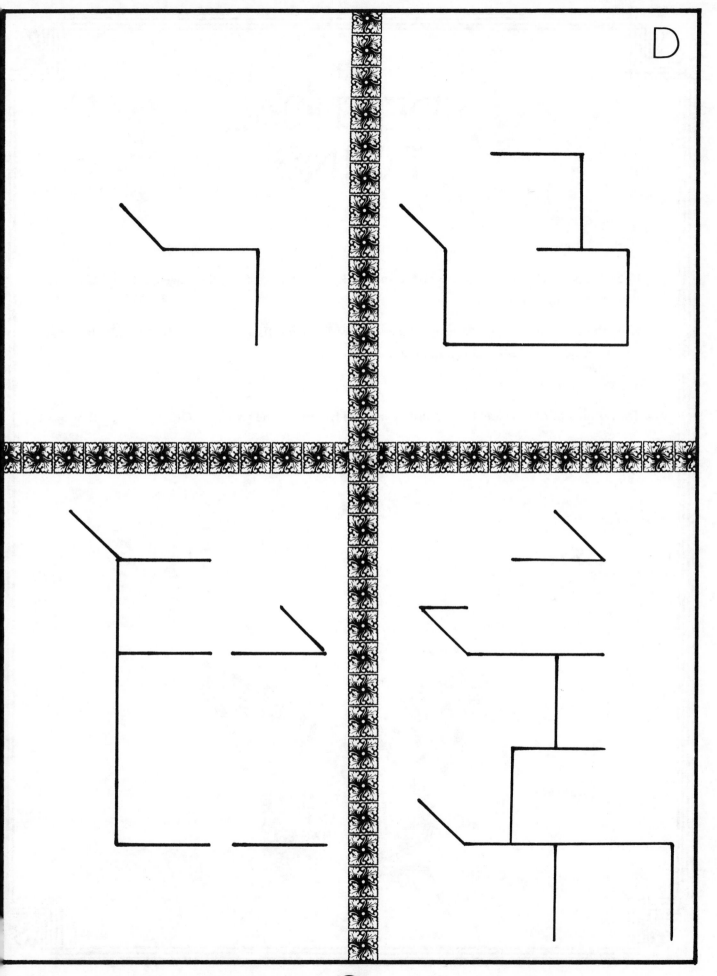

D

IDENTICAL
TWINS

Skills: Pattern identification, analytical seeing, synthesizing visually, visual recall.

In each case (with the exception of the snowflakes) each page or double page has two sets of identical twins. Can you find them?

Have these duplicated on overheads. Place on overhead and flash them quickly for your class. Turn the overhead on and off quickly and see if anyone can see the twins.

Turn it on for a little bit longer.

Turn it on a third time and leave it until everyone has found the twins . . . OR

Duplicate the pages and let students work on them individually.

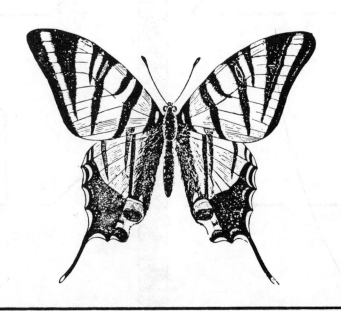

1.

2.

3.

4.

5.

6.

On the next double-page spread there are two sets of twins. Can you find them?

The rabbit above matches one of the rabbits on the next two pages. Can you see which one that is?

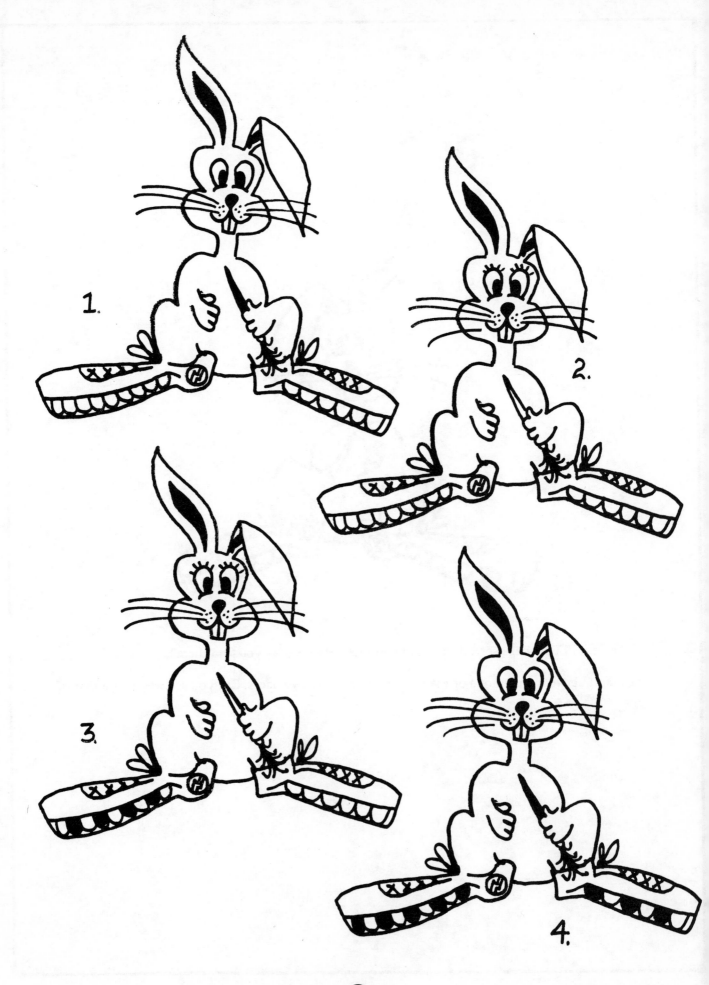

1.

2.

3.

4.

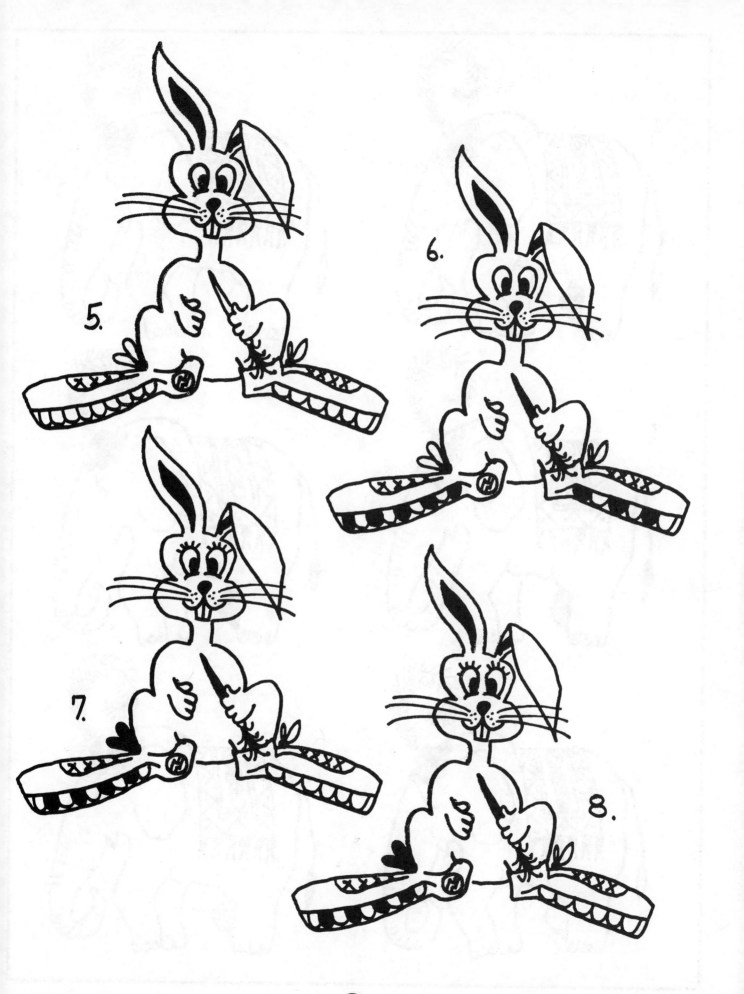

5.

6.

7.

8.

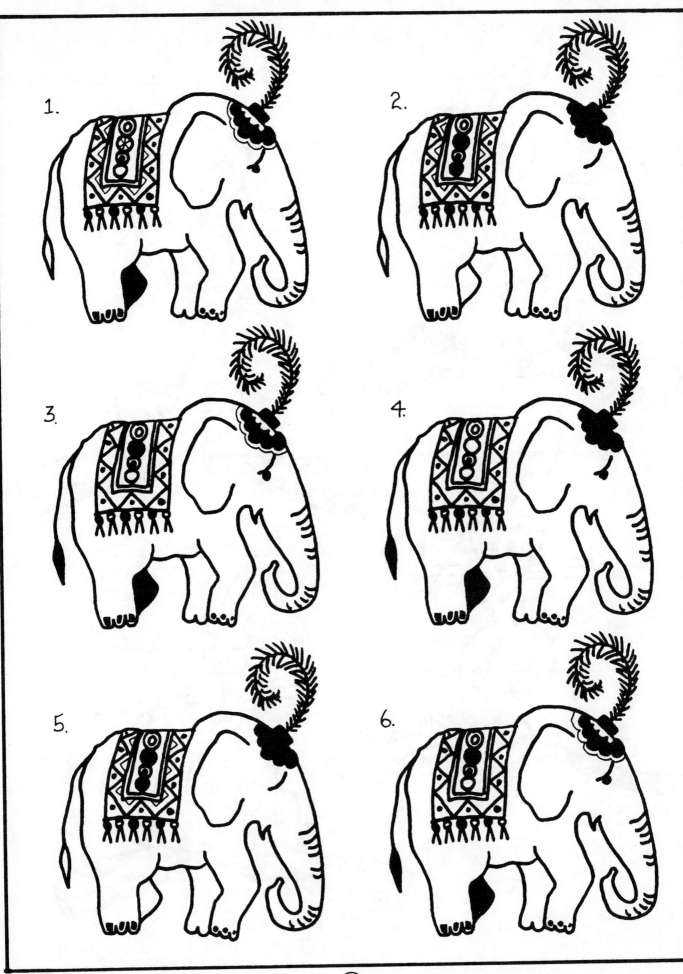

On each of the next double-page spreads you will find ONE set of twins. Can you see them?

Does the snowflake above match any of the following snowflakes?

1

2

5

6

3

4

7

8

DISCREPANT DETAILS

●

Take each of the following pages and put them on a bulletin board as the problem for the week.

Each design has had some changes made that destroy the symmetry . . . in other words, they have been made inconsistent.

See if your students can find those inconsistencies.

Encourage them not to give away the answers when they find them, but to let everyone have a chance to try.

Page A   Each design has 3 changes

Page B   This design has 3 changes

Page C   Each design has 1 change

Page D   Each design has 3 changes

Page E   Each design has 3 changes

Page F   This design has 3 changes

Page G   Each design has 1 change

Page H   This design has 3 changes

After you have worked all of these, let students take pictures from magazines or their own pictures, make small "errors" in them and see if the other students can find the discrepancies.

A

B

C

Each of these designs has one detail that is not the same as the rest of the design. Can you spot it?

101

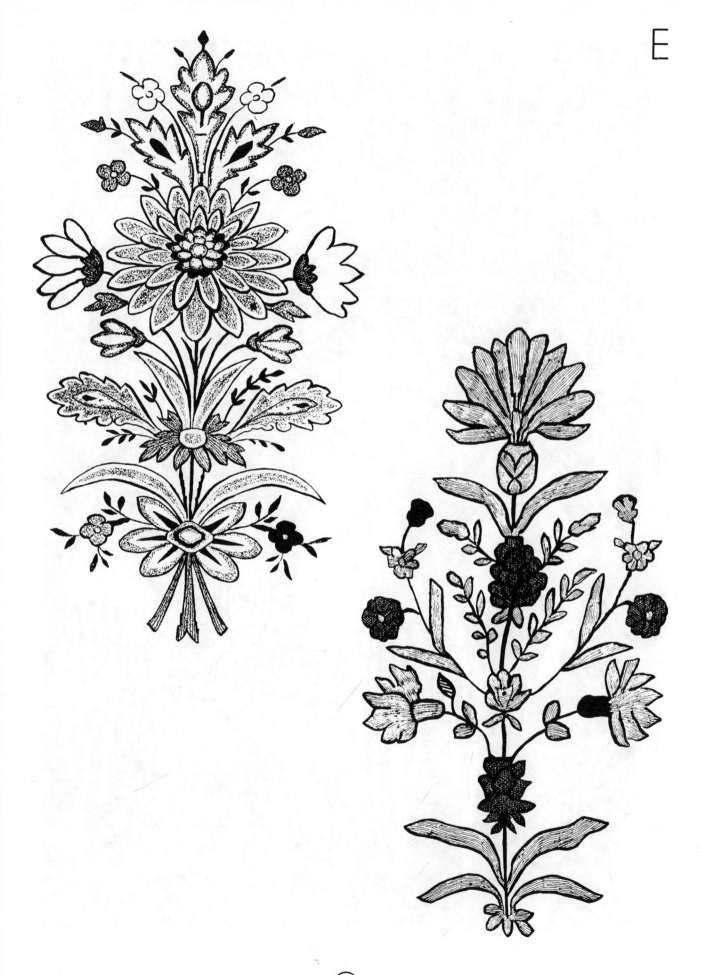

F

G

●mirroring

Duplicate the following pages for your students.

The "A" Pages

On each of these pages the student is to duplicate the design in reverse, making it as close to the original as possible . . . only just the opposite.

If they have trouble, have some small hand mirrors handy. When placed along the axis line and at right angles to the page, you will be able to see how the design should look when completed.

Encourage them to work without rulers or other measuring devices.

Students can then make up more of these and try them out on each other.

The "B" Pages

These are the same as the ones above except that we are now working with two axis lines.

The first one is completed to show how it would look.

Again, a small hand mirror might help some students in approaching these problems in perception.

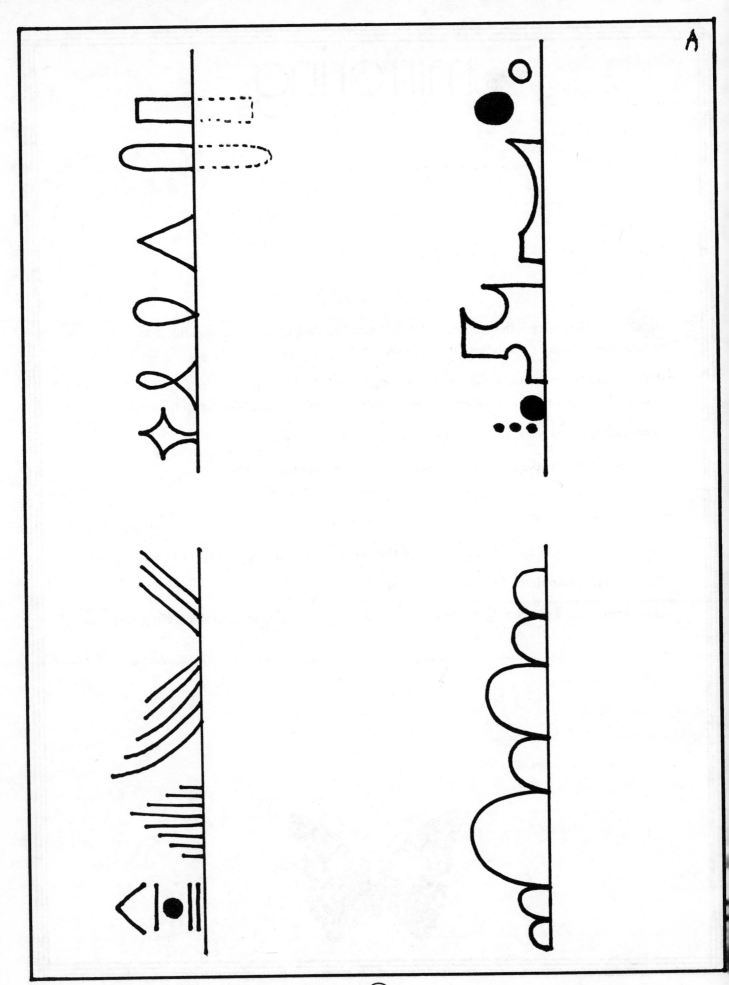

A.

(110)

A.

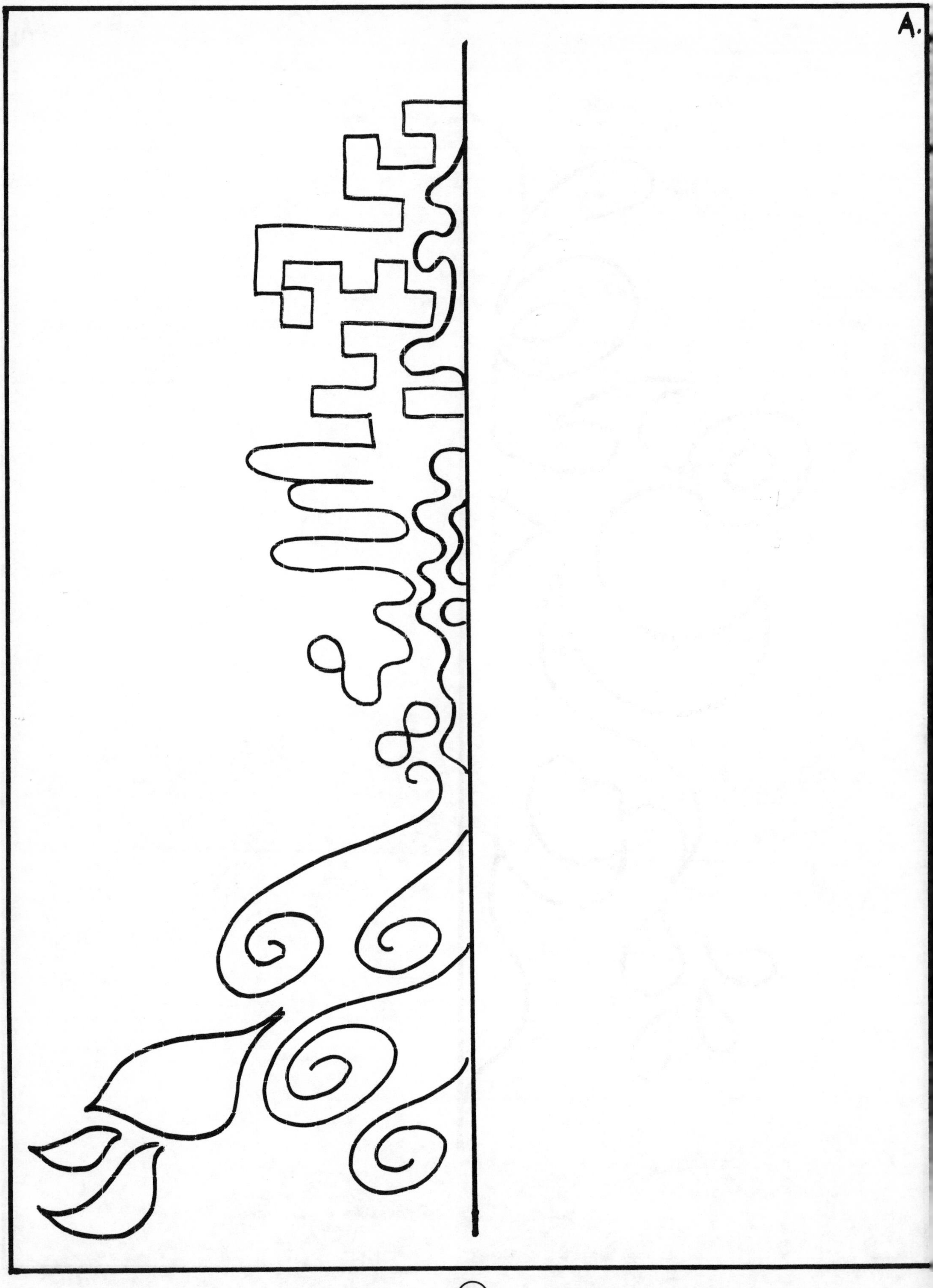

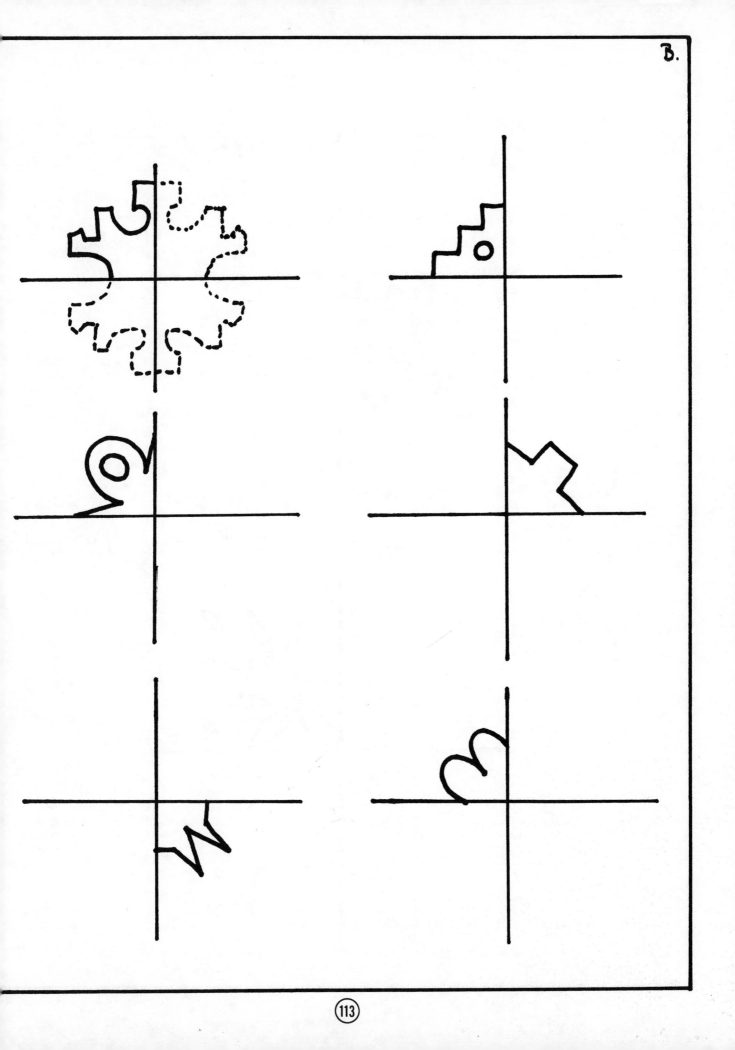

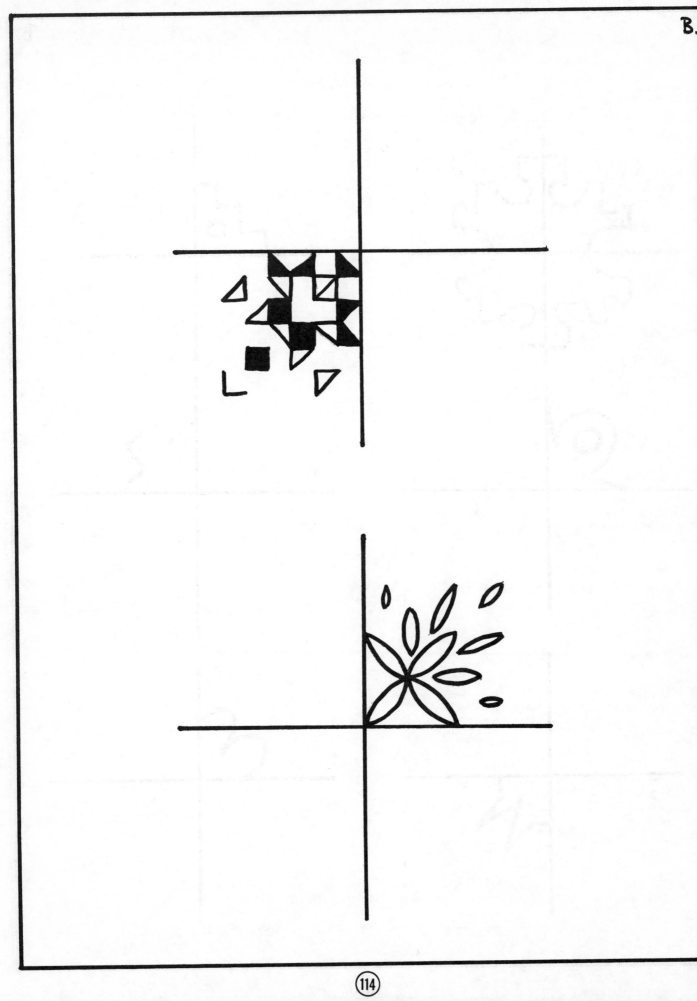

B.

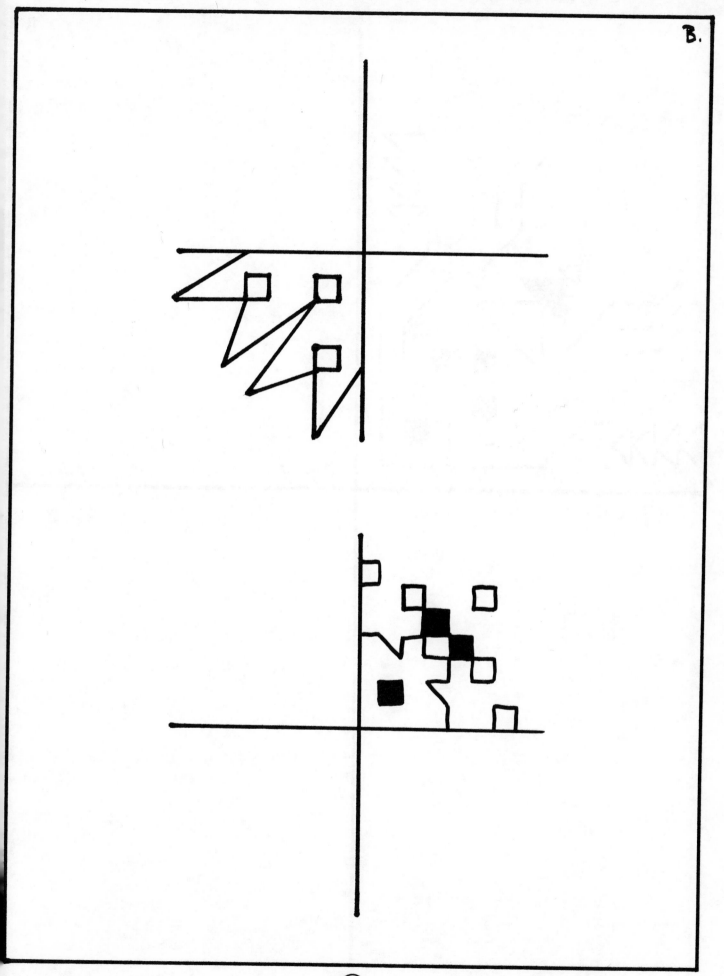

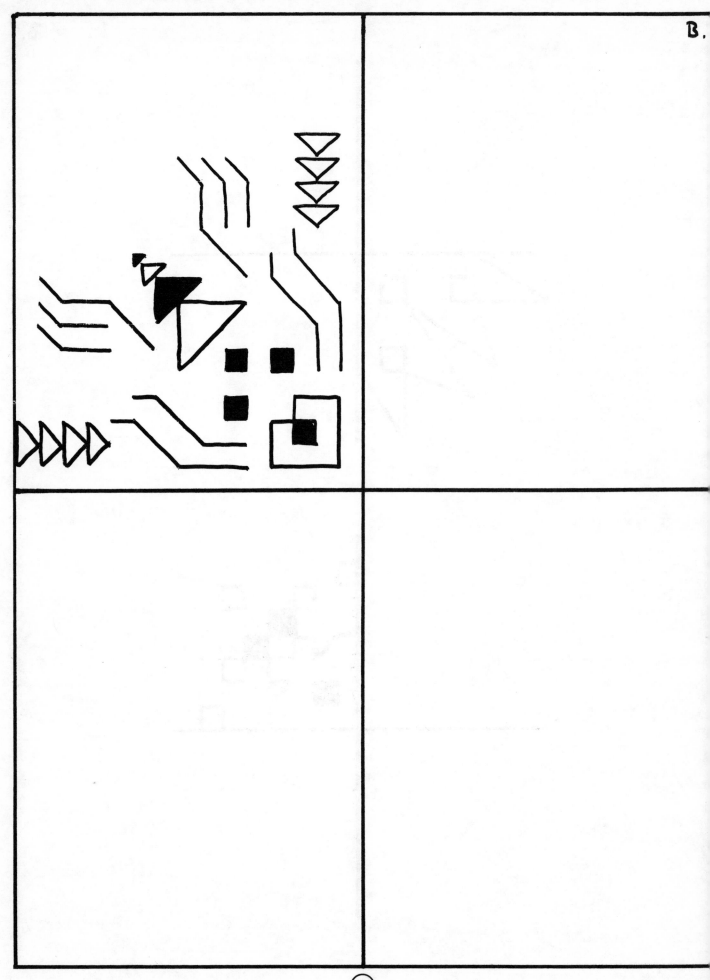

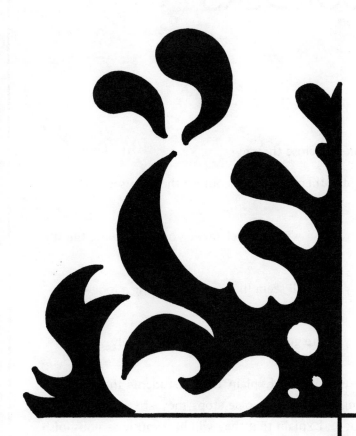

IMAGE BUILDERS

●

First, encourage students to get comfortable, relax and close their eyes.

Explain that you are going to describe something for them to see. Encourage them to see it as clearly as they can.

Read each fantasy slowly and clearly. Be sure to pause with each element you add, giving the students time to really "see" it in their mind.

Give them more time than you think is necessary. . .it will seem like you are waiting a long time. . . allow at least 10 seconds between each idea.

After you have done one or two, ask your class if you are going too quickly or too slowly.

Note: BUTTERFLY is a little different from the others. Explain to the students that you will describe a setting and the beginning of something. When your voice stops, they are to let the story complete itself in their own mind as they so choose. Explain that they will hear music as you finish speaking, tell them to continue the story in their own mind until they begin to notice the music fading. Then they can bring the story to a close as the music disappears.

THE MIND'S EYE

Close your eyes. Try to visualize what I am going to describe to you as clearly as you can. See a square. It is about 8 inches on a side. It is green. In the middle of the square you can see a red heart. In the upper left-hand corner of the square is a circle. It is yellow. In the upper right-hand corner is a triangle. It is orange. Now look down at the lower left-hand corner. There you will see a nose. It has a cold. Poor nose. And in the lower-right hand corner you will see a very old shoe. It has been tossed away as it is almost worn out. Can you see that entire picture in your mind? The square with the heart in the middle, the yellow circle, the orange triangle, the nose with a cold, and a very old shoe? . . . Good. Now . . . put the circle where the nose is . . . put the nose where the triangle is . . . and put the triangle where the circle was. Leave the shoe in place. Change the color of the heart from red to purple and see something very beautiful in its center. Can you see your new picture? See it as clearly as you can . . . Good. Now open your eyes and draw a picture of what you are seeing at this moment.

TEDDY BEAR

Close your eyes. See a brand new teddy bear. It is soft and plump and fat. It is golden brown . . . wearing a bright blue jacket with two tiny pockets and yellow trim. Mr. Teddy has black button eyes, a small brown nose and a bright pink tongue that just barely sticks out of his mouth. And he is smiling such a happy smile. Now watch Mr. Teddy change . . . he is a Teddy Bear that gets a lot of love and he is beginning to get old. He is getting older and older as you watch. His bright blue jacket is fading. Oh dear, a pocket is torn and part of his jacket is coming unsewn. One of Teddy's ears is missing and some stuffing is squeezing out of the hole. Someone who loves him keeps poking it back in. One of Teddy's eyes fell off long ago and the other one is very loose and could be lost at any moment. Teddy's tongue is no longer bright pink . . . it is sort of dull gray. . . much of the color has faded over the years . . . but he still has a very happy smile on his face because someone loves him very much. . . . . .

Open your eyes and draw (paint) a picture of Teddy as you can see him right now . . . Go ahead . . . If you have trouble, close your eyes and see him again in your mind . . . be sure to see all the changes he has gone through in his long and much loved life.

(You may also have students draw or paint Teddy as described when brand new.)

NEW WORLD

Close your eyes . . . you can see a new world. It is an unusual and almost barren landscape. The sky is red, violet and orange . . . the soil is almost the same color and they seem to melt into one another at the horizon . . . In the far distance are the gray and black silhouettes of gnarled and twisted trees growing wild and free and dark against the sky. Nothing is moving. You are alone in this empty red world. You look up into the sky and are suddenly startled by a large animal soaring toward you on outspread wings. It is huge. Its wings are like gossamer . . . like the wings of a dragon-fly out-stretched to each side. But wait . . . it reminds you of an elephant . . . an elephant with wings . . . its ears look more like the wings of a bat and they, too, are outstretched as if to keep this creature balanced in the sky. Instead of the feet of an elephant, this creature has large hooked feet . . . more like giant talons with which it can clutch at branches and rocks when it seeks to land. Two long and pointed tusks protude from either side of its jaw and curve sharply inward toward each other. Its eyes glow fire-red like the coals of a dying fire. You can hear the rush of the wind as its wings beat upon the air. It glides like a whisper over your head and is suddenly . . . gone. It wishes you no harm . . . for it is a very gentle creature. Only in its looks does it appear fearsome. You are alone again in a silent red world . . .

(You may have students first create just the landscape . . . say on a bulletin board. Encourage them to make it as imaginative as possible. Repeat the experience and have them get in groups to create the flying creatures as they saw them in their minds. These can then be cut out and placed in the sky of your "strange, new-world bulletin board.")

Some vocabulary you may wish to explore before taking this journey:

barren	twisted	clutch
violet	startled	protrude
horizon	soaring	landscape
silhouettes	gossamer	
gnarled	talons	

THE BUG

Close your eyes. You are standing on the grass in a beautiful forest. Walk slowly over to a tree and look closely at it. There is a branch at your eye level. Walk up to it and notice that sitting on that branch . . . out near the end is a BUG. It is a very unusual bug . . . it has a shiny body that glows, glitters and shines almost as if it were electric, and it shines in your very favorite color. This special bug has six velvet covered legs . . . soft golden brown, the color of toast just the way you like it . . . its feet are tiny, tiny claws that hold tightly to the branch. See its body, its legs and claws . . . three claws on each foot . . . now look at its head. Its head is very beautiful. It is shiny black like ebony. It has two large lime-green eyes with crimson centers . . . with long soft lashes like feathers. Two very long feelers grow out of the top of its head. The ends of these feelers look like tiny umbrellas that are full open to shade Mr. Bug from the sun or from the rain. Mr. Bug is smiling. He has four transparent wings that grow from his back and he has been waiting for them to dry, for they are very new. They glisten and sparkle in the light. They look blue and green and pink all at the same time. Mr. Bug is slowly waving his wings now. Testing them gently. Now faster and faster. Suddenly he lifts from the branch and flies in a lazy circle all around you . . . now higher and higher and higher . . . so high into the bright blue sky that you lose sight of him as he disappears into the sky . . . .

(Paint Mr. Bug exactly as you saw him. OR sculpt him from clay and when the clay is dry . . . paint him. . . OR make him from papier maché.

Teacher: This can also be done from the point of view of the students being the bug. It would be changed in this manner: You are a beautiful, beautiful bug. You are sitting on the branch of a tree in the middle of a lush, green forest. Your body is very unusual. You have a shiny body that glows, glitters, and shines almost as if it were electric. Your body is your very favorite color. You have six velvet covered legs . . . etc., etc.)

Some vocabulary you may want to discuss or illustrate before you do this exercise:

shiny	velvet	lashes
glitters	ebony	transparent
electric	crimson	glisten

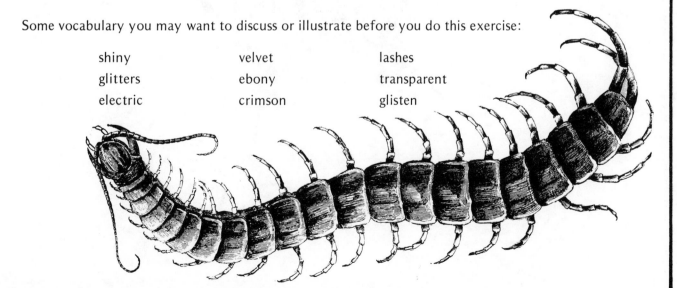

BUTTERFLY

Close your eyes. See yourself walking through the winter woods. It is midnight and you are alone. It is very cold and very still. The only sounds you hear are those of your own feet crunching through the crusty snow, and the sound of your breath as it hits the icy air and turns to frosty mist and floats away. You are bundled in fur. Deep rich fur mittens, parka, leggings and boots. You are warm and comfortable inside your thick, fur clothes as you walk. The trees are bare and black against a stark, midnight sky. The stars shine like bright diamonds . . . hard and cold against the black backdrop. The stillness is all around you. You are walking slowly through the woods. Empty. Still. Frozen. Now you notice ahead of you, through the trees a ball of light. It is golden and pulsates with a life of its own. As you get closer, you can see in the center of that ball of light a golden butterfly gently drying its wings. It has just begun life. You move closer and closer to the light, and as you step into its circle of light, you feel an unexpected warmth. Everything is golden . . . and warm . . . you come closer and closer . . . . . .

(At this point, stop the narration and fade in some music of your choice that seems to fit the mood. Allow students to finish what happens in their own mind. Give them perhaps five minutes; then begin to fade the music out. When it is silent, give them another minute; then have them sit up and share what happened in their own private story with a neighbor.)

●POTPOURRI

Skills: All of the skills are used in this section.

Here are a few miscellaneous pages of visual problems.

Make overheads of them for use with the entire class, or duplicate for students to work on alone or in small groups.

The pages are self-explanatory with the exception of the elephant and the man in armor. For each of these, the student looks at the picture until he/she is sure he/she knows it. Turns it over and answers all the questions to the best of his/her ability. This can then be done with newspaper photos and pictures from books and magazines. Students can pick the pictures and make up the questions to go with the pictures.

3 views of the same cube:

What is opposite
the hand?

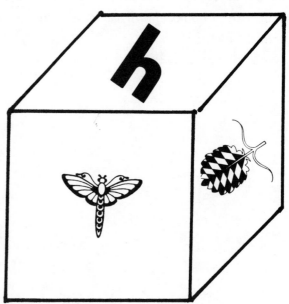

What is opposite
the bug?

What is opposite
the lion?

Study this page until you know it.

Turn page and answer the questions.

Do <u>not</u> look back at the picture
for reference.

How many elephants are in the picture?

How many of them have tusks?

What is in the sky behind the elephants?

Which elephant has one foot raised?

Which foot is it?

What is under the foot that is raised?

Is the largest elephant facing more to its left or to its right?

Is the largest elephant's trunk curling under or up?

What other kind of animal is shown in the picture?

Study this page. Turn page and answer the questions. Do <u>NOT</u> look back at this page.

What is the figure in the picture holding in its left hand?

Is the other hand holding anything at all?

What is the location of the right hand?

Is the figure a man or a woman?

Does the figure have a mustache? Beard? Neither? Both?

Describe in as much detail as you can what the figure's shoes look like.

What are on the figure's shoulders?

Is the object the figure is holding stuck into the ground or resting upon the ground?

Is there a sunburst on the figures chest?

On each of the following **3** pages, if you were to pick up each rope by the ends and pull, which ones would have knots in them and which ones would not?

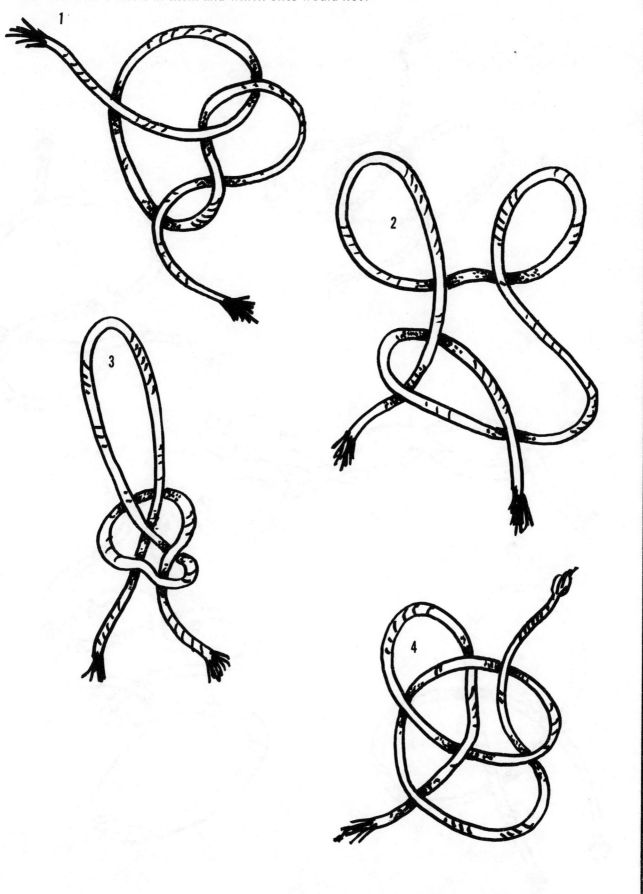

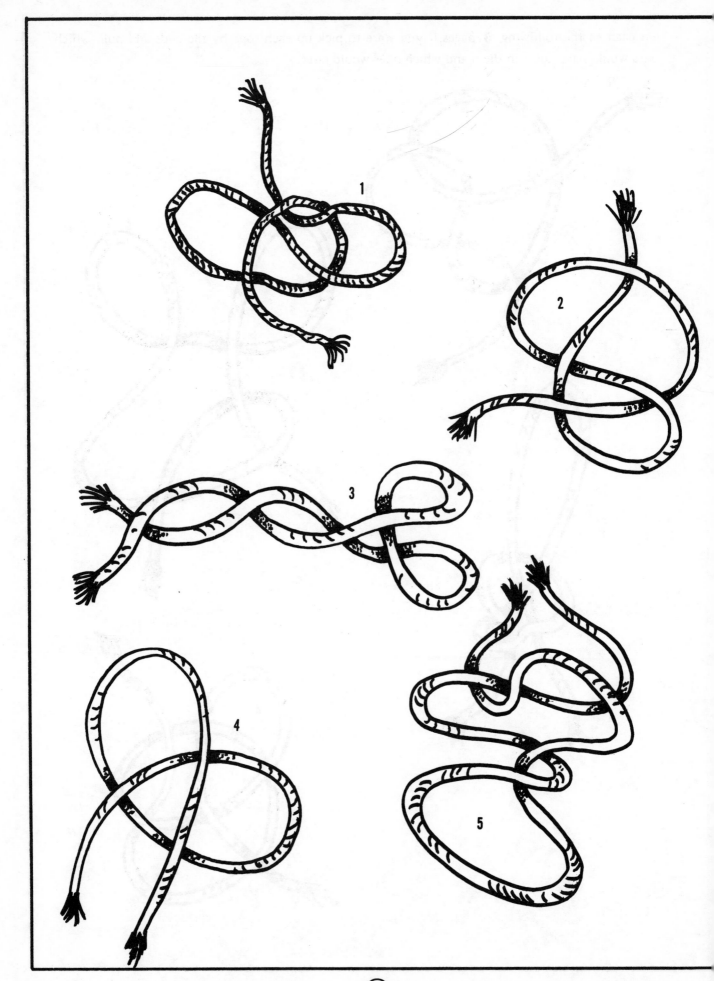

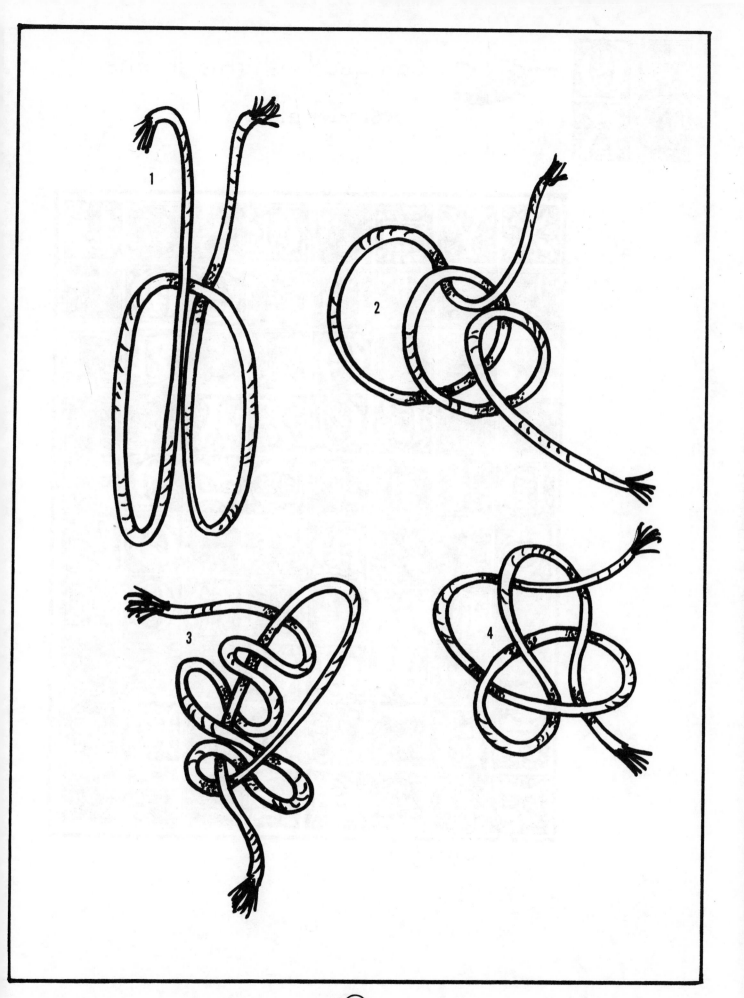

 Can you find this in the design below?

On the following pages you will find drawings . . . sort of!

Either duplicate the pages or put one up on the bulletin board.

Encourage children to look at them from all directions and make a list of all the things they see in the drawing.

When you have done all of the pages in this section, students can make their own in the following manner. Place a sheet of tracing paper over a photograph (preferably from large color or blk & wht. magazines. Using a marker, darken in all of the LIGHT areas. NOTE: Do NOT darken in the shadows! DO darken in the highlights!) When this is done, tape the resulting drawing to a piece of white tag board and hang them for each other to examine and determine what they are.

Turn the drawings around and view them from all directions.

Make a list of all the things you can see in each one.

BIBLIOGRAPHY

The following materials will expand and develop the skills introduced and encouraged in *The Other Side of Reading: The Forgotten Skills.*

Art: Of A Wonder and A World, Art. Ed. Inc., Blauvelt, N.Y. 10913.

Be a Frog, a Bird, or a Tree, Rachael Carr, Doubleday, Garden City, N.Y.

Classroom Ideas for Thinking and Feeling, Frank Williams, D.O.K. Publishers, 71 Radcliffe Road, Buffalo, N.Y. 14214.

Complete Book of Children's Theater, Vernon Howard, Doubleday and Co.

Cricket's Tangrams, M. Peek, Random House, '77.

Doodling Your Way to Better Recall, L. Smith, Academic Therapy Publishers, Novato, CA 94947.

Experiences in Visual Learning, McKim, Brooks/Cole, Monterey, CA.

GOOD APPLE MATERIALS

Secrets and Surprises, Joe Wayman and Lorraine Plum, Good Apple, Box 299, Carthage, IL 62321.

Sunflowering, Bob Stanish.

I Believe in Unicorns, Bob Stanish.

Imagination and Me, Joe Wayman and Don Mitchell, Ibid. (album)

Dandy-Lions Never Roar, Joe Wayman and Don Mitchell, Ibid. (album)

Ballad of Lucy Lum, Don Mitchell and Joe Wayman, Ibid. (album)

Colors of My Rainbow, Joe Wayman, Ibid. (album)

(Activity and music books by the same titles are also available.)

Invisibles   Troubador Press, 485 Fremont St., San Francisco, CA.

Which One is Different   Ibid.

Maze Craze   Ibid.

Making it Strange, Harper and Row, 49 E. 33rd. St., N.Y. 10016.

New Games Book, Flueglman, Doubleday, '76.

One Hundred Involving Art Projects, N. Laliberté, Art Ed. Inc., Blauvelt, N.Y.

One Hundred Ways to Have Fun With an Alligator, Ibid.

Opt-Iddles, R. Heller, Golden Press.

Put Your Mother On the Ceiling, Richard de Mille, Penguin Paper Backs.

Puzzle Blast, L. Fellows, Scholastic.

Flights of Fantasy, Lorraine Plum, Good Apple, 1980.

Scamper, Bob Eberle, D.O.K., Buffalo, N.Y.

Shadowplay, George Mendoza, Holt, Rinehart and Winston, N.Y.

Sometimes I Dance Mountains, Byrd Baylor, Scribner's Sons, N.Y.

Startrek Intergalactic Puzzles, J. Razzi, Bantam.

Startrek Puzzle Manual,   Ibid.

Strange and Familiar, Porpoise Books.

Theater Game File, Viola Spolin, CEMREL, 3120 59th St., St. Louis, MO 63139.

Development Through Drama, Brian Way, Humanities Press, Atlantic Highlands, N.Y.

Would You Rather Be a Bullfrog?, Theo LeSieg, Random House, N.Y.

Yoga For All Ages, Rachael Carr, Simon and Schuster.

Research

Magical Child, Joseph Pearce, Dutton, '77.

Beyond Biofeedback, Green & Green, Delacorte, '77.

Mind and Supermind, A. Rosenfeld, Holt, Rhinehart & Winston, '77.

Farther Reaches of Human Nature, Maslow, Viking, '71.

Psychology of Consciousness, Ornstein, Penguin, '72.

Metaphoric Mind, Samples, Adison Wesley, '76.

Use Both Sides of Your Brain, T. Buzan, Dutton, '74.

SOLUTIONS

HOW MANY

p.**20**   eight
p.**21**   five
p.**22**   seventeen
p.**24**   you figure these out
p.**25**   Highest count so far is eighty nine.
p.**26**   23
p.**27**   19
p.**28**   At least 35
p.**29**   45

TANGRAMS

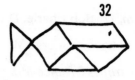

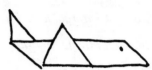

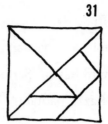

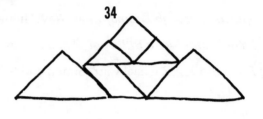

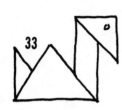

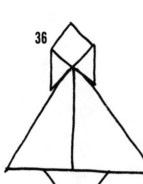

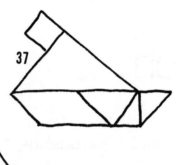

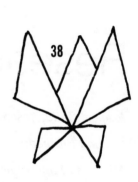

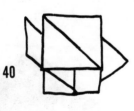

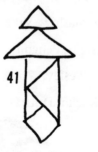

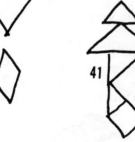

SHAPE UP!

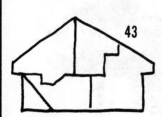

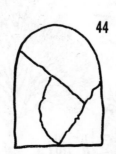

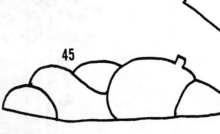

140

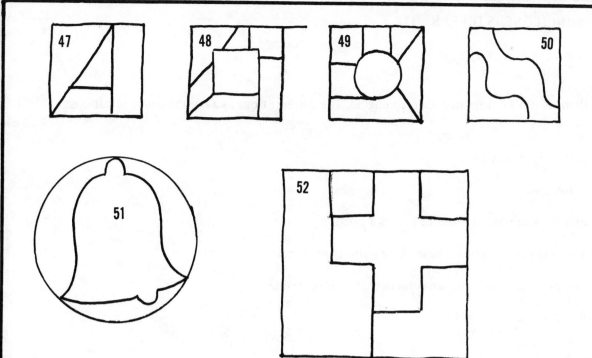

CONGRUENT FIGURES

53
1. yes
2. yes
3. no
4. yes

54
1. yes
2. no
3. yes
4. no
5. no
6. yes
7. yes
8. yes
9. no

55
1. yes
2. yes
3. no
4. yes
5. no
6. yes
7. no
8. yes
9. no

56
1. yes
2. yes
3. yes
4. yes
5. yes
6. no
7. no
8. yes
9. yes

57
1. yes
2. no
3. no
4. yes
5. yes
6. yes
7. no
8. yes
9. yes

TRAINS 59

Only one of them is not or does not have an engine. The different one is a combination of caboose and tank car.

Only one is a direct head-on view.

Only one is the longest.

Only one is not a train or part of a train . . . it is a bird!

Only one has two engines hooked together facing the same direction.

Only one is a self-powered maintanence vehicle that runs on tracks.

Only one shows passenger cars.

Can you think of any more different ones?

GEOMETRIC SHAPES 60

Only one is a square.

Only one has one indented angle.

Only one has two indented angles.

Only one touches another one.

Only one has seven sides.

Can you think of some other ways one may be different?

AMOEBAS 61

One has no center.

One has two separate centers.

One has two concentric centers.

One is a circle.

One has a dark center.

ANIMALS 62

One has NO legs.

One has gills.

One is domestic.

One is a skeleton.

One has the longest neck.

One is hanging by its tail.

One has a shell.

One is looking directly at you.

RABBITS 63

Only one is spotted.

You can see both eyes in only one.

Only one is lifting just the left paw.

Only one is lifting just the right paw.

Other differences???

LETTERS 64

Only one has no serifs. (look up "serifs" with the class) . . . it is the large "K" near the middle.

Only one is an "A."

Only one is a number. (4)

Only one is the biggest.

VEGETABLES 65

Only one is a berry.

Only one grows as separate "stalks."

Only one is tied together.

Only one is a bulb.

Only one is primarily eaten for the leaves.

How are the berry and the carrot the same?

How are the corn and the peas the same?

Can you think up some more questions about this page?

ANIMAL DESIGNS 66

Only one has no animal.

Only one has antlers.

Only one is a horse, rabbit, snake, etc. . . .

Can you find others that are different from the rest?

73

74

75

76

81

77

IDENTICAL TWINS

83 Giraffes
1 & 7
4 & 9

84 Dragons
2 & 6
3 & 4

86 – 87
Rabbits
4 & 6
7 & 8

88 Elephants
3 & 6
3 & 5

snowflakes: You'll have to find these on your own!

94 Designs
6 & 5
1 & 4

96 – 97
Faces
6 & 4
2 & 5

DISCREPANT DETAILS

No solutions given. But you will have at least one student who will find all the changes . . . guaranteed!

POTPOURRI

ROPES

p. 129		p. 130	
1. yes		1. no	
2. yes		2. yes	
3. no		3. no	
4. yes		4. no	
		5. no	

p. 131   1. no   2. no   3. no   4. yes

133 Toothpaste, two brushes in a cup

134 Sea shell
Side view of a face

135 Sheep
Orange halves with knife

136 Person talking on telephone
Bare foot with cuff balancing on bamboo

137 Ear with earring
Child on bicycle